"It's . . . Alive!"

Lex Luthor shouted with joy, reaching to punch open the lock on the laboratory door. "Now, watch, Lenny. See how he obeys my commands."

Lex stood up and walked over to Nuclear Man. "I created you for one reason only," he told him, tapping a picture of Superman. "To destroy this man!"

Nuclear Man's face lit up with the joy of understanding. His mouth opened tortuously, and he spoke.

"Yes . . . F-f-faaather!"

WARNER BROS. PRESENTS

CHRISTOPHER REEVE · GENE HACKMAN

IN A CANNON GROUP·GOLAN/GLOBUS PRODUCTION OF A SIDNEY J. FURIE FILM SUPERMAN IV

JACKIE COOPER · MARC McCLURE · JON CRYER · SAM WANAMAKER · MARK PILLOW WITH MARIEL HEMINGWAY
AND MARGOT KIDDER AS LOIS LANE VISUAL EFFECTS SUPERVISOR HARRISON ELLENSHAW DIRECTOR OF PHOTOGRAPHY ERNEST DAY, B.S.C. PRODUCTION DESIGNER JOHN GRAYSMARK
ASSOCIATE PRODUCERS MICHAEL KAGAN AND GRAHAM EASTON STORY BY CHRISTOPHER REEVE AND LAWRENCE KONNER & MARK ROSENTHAL
SCREENPLAY BY LAWRENCE KONNER & MARK ROSENTHAL PRODUCED BY MENAHEM GOLAN AND YORAM GLOBUS DIRECTED BY SIDNEY J. FURIE

SUPERMAN IV

A novelization by B.B. Hiller. Based on the
story by Christopher Reeve and Lawrence Konner
& Mark Rosenthal, and screenplay by
Lawrence Konner & Mark Rosenthal.

SCHOLASTIC INC.
New York Toronto London Auckland Sydney

For Emmons B. Hiller

ISBN 0-590-41195-0

12 11 10 9 8 7 6 5 4 3 2 1   7 8 9/8 0 1 2/9

Printed in the U.S.A   01

First Scholastic printing, July 1987

Prologue

Thousands of miles below, Earth dangled invitingly, as if suspended, against the velvet black of the void.

The man sighed and resumed his work outside the space capsule, repairing the main radio antenna. He was a Russian cosmonaut, and until he fixed it, he and his comrades had no way to communicate with Earth. They were about as alone as any four people could possibly be.

Slowly and carefully, encumbered by the oversize space suit, he maneuvered to the other side of the antenna. He had a job to do. He sang to himself as he worked. The song was an American song called "My Way."

From inside the capsule, the captain called out to his comrade on the intercom. "Spare us the serenade, Comrade Sinatra," he teased. "You're not at home."

"At home, my kids tell me to save my singing

for outer space!" His comrades laughed. He resumed his work. Silently.

And silently, his doom approached. Tumbling through space at unimaginable speed, impelled by perpetual motion, there came a chunk of debris, the forgotten remains of a failed experiment in space.

The debris struck both the cosmonaut and the ship at almost the exact instant he and his comrades saw it. Its force was so compelling and the impact so great that the entire capsule was thrown out of its orbit. It tumbled out of control. The cosmonauts whirled within it.

The cosmonaut outside spun helplessly, Earth and void merging into a blackness that separated him from his comrades more and more with every turn.

"I'm lost! Farewell! *Dasvidanya!*" he cried bravely, and without hope.

But suddenly, something happened. Suddenly, as the cosmonaut watched, his comrades' capsule stopped spinning. Suddenly, the capsule moved back where it belonged. Suddenly, it returned to its programmed route and resumed its orbit.

"How could that be?" he asked out loud, watching the miracle with his own eyes. And suddenly, he knew.

It was Superman!

For there he was. Superman's face shone with resolve and strength — ever calm in the heat of crisis — always there when the citizens of Earth needed him most.

Smoothly, Superman turned from the capsule to rescue the cosmonaut. Within seconds, Superman had caught up to him and took him gently in his strong arms. He carried the cosmonaut back to the capsule, returning him to the ship's air lock.

"I think you'll be safer in here, sir," Superman told the cosmonaut, who nodded in astonishment and relief.

Then, while the cosmonaut watched, Superman corrected the pitch of the capsule's radio antenna and sealed the repair with his heat vision. He nodded acknowledgment to the cosmonaut's wave and then left, as swiftly and silently as he'd come.

For he had other promises to keep.

Chapter 1

Clark Kent gazed sadly at the FOR SALE sign in front of the farmhouse where he had been raised by George and Martha Kent. They were both dead now and Clark had moved to Metropolis, where he had a job as a reporter for the *Daily Planet*. It was time to sell the farm.

But before he sold it, he had something to take care of.

The vessel that had brought him to Earth from Krypton those many years ago had to be hidden — permanently. Clark had no place to put it, and he couldn't permit the farm's new owners to find it accidentally. That would risk revealing his true identity as Superman.

After putting fresh flowers on Ma and Pa Kent's graves, Clark returned to the barn. In no time, he had dug a deep hole. Satisfied that it would hide his secret forever, he went to the hayloft where the vessel was stored. He had seen the dust of an approaching car on the road.

He had only a few minutes to complete his task.

Clark brushed the hay off the old tarp and lifted the canvas cover. There was the metallic carcass of the ship that had carried him so long ago. He lifted it easily and set it in the newly dug hole. But before he could cover it again, there was a glow, green and eerie. It was the familiar green of Krypton. Then a voice emitted from the ship's control panel.

". . . the yellow sun of your new home," the voice said.

"Father!" Clark uttered, recognizing Jor-El's voice from across the years.

The voice continued mechanically. ". . . Placed aboard this vessel is an energy module — all that remains of Krypton, your mother planet. It is my last gift to you. Once removed, the ship will grow cold and silent, and you will finally be alone. The power of the module can be used but once. Use it wisely, my son."

The message ended. The vessel glowed green and then darkened. Clark reached into the control panel and retrieved the module. Then he stepped away from the vessel and climbed up out of the pit he had dug. A whirlwind followed him out of the hole, filling in the hole completely.

When at last the dust settled, Clark held the module tightly, knowing it was his final connection with his home planet.

"Clark! You in there?"

The voice came from the driveway. Clark

knew it was the real estate agent who would sell the farm for him.

"Hello, Mr. Hornsby. It's been a long time." Clark offered his hand. "I've just been tidying up for when you show the place," Clark said, explaining his presence.

"Didn't I mention that there was an offer to buy already — *sight unseen?*"

That was what Clark had been afraid might happen. Anybody who would buy that land without even looking at it couldn't possibly care about it. It had to be a big developer.

"I'm sorry," Clark said politely. "But I don't want to sell the farm to a developer. Whoever buys it has to want to keep a working farm. I don't think we need another shopping center," he explained.

Hornsby frowned in frustration. "Darn it, Clark Kent. Why are you so stubborn? Today, nobody wants a farm. That's progress!" He strolled into the barn to look around.

Suddenly, Clark was afraid he'd find a trace of the vessel he'd hidden so quickly. He ran into the barn after Mr. Hornsby. But there was no hint of the Kryptonian capsule.

Hornsby looked around the barn, his eyes lighting on a dusty crib. Its sturdy wooden headboard was neatly broken in half. Mr. Hornsby laughed, recalling something. "What a joker your dad was," he mused. "I asked your dad one day once what happened to this crib.

He said to me, real casual, you know, 'Oh, Clark must have kicked it.' "

Clark laughed along with him. "Dad always liked a good joke," he said, ushering Mr. Hornsby back to his car.

When Hornsby's car had disappeared in the dust on the long country road, Clark picked up his bat and baseball from high school. He tossed the ball into the air and took a swing at it with the bat.

CRACK!

"Home run!" he cried proudly. The ball sailed endlessly into the sky, gone forever — and with it, Clark Kent's youth, on Earth and Krypton.

Chapter 2

Superman's greatest daily challenge was maintaining his disguise as Clark Kent. He had to be the bumbling but kindly reporter, or he'd be unmasked, undermining all his work on Earth. Even for Superman, it was a difficult task to be the Man of Steel but pretend to be a weakling.

The phone rang in Clark's Metropolis apartment. Before Clark could get to it, his answering machine responded. Then he heard a rushed and ominous message from Lois Lane, colleague and star reporter for the *Daily Planet*.

"Clark, I hope you're up. Perry wants us in the office *on time*. Something big is going on. *Au revoir*."

Clark jumped for the phone, and said "Hello," hoping to get a hint from Lois about what the excitement was at the office, but she had hung up. He was talking to a dial tone.

Perry White, editor in chief of the *Daily*

Planet, and Lois and Clark's irascible boss, didn't often call early morning staff meetings. Clark was curious. He got an idea of what might be up as he ate his breakfast and listened to the radio.

". . . And, in the news, we have word that the East-West arms control talks have broken down. The President is scheduled to address the nation later."

Clark grabbed his jacket and briefcase. Lois was right. He had to hurry.

As usual, the subway station was crammed with people. It seemed to take forever just to get into the station. Superman might have flown, but Clark Kent waited patiently for his turn to wait to buy a token so he could wait to get through the turnstile before waiting for a subway. When he was almost at the turnstile, a train pulled into the station. He knew he wouldn't catch that train.

But Lois did. She spotted Clark through the crowd and waved gaily at him before she boarded the subway car. His hands were full. He waved back with the hand carrying his briefcase, hitting himself in the head with it, and knocking his glasses askew.

Good old Clark, Lois thought, watching him through the window of the subway car as it carried her out of the station.

Even as Clark adjusted his glasses, he sensed something was wrong. Squinting, he used his

X-ray vision, following the subway car into the tunnel. There, in the very front car, Clark watched as the engineer paled in agony, clutching his chest. Quickly, Clark scanned the entire subway. He saw Lois and thousands of other passengers unmindful of impending disaster. Clark gasped involuntarily.

This was a job for Superman!

Clark ripped off his glasses and ran toward the tunnel. Moving faster than human eyes could see, Clark changed from his pinstriped suit to Superman's outfit as he followed the subway whose next stop could be catastrophe.

Superman sprang into the air and shot after the subway with determination. Quickly, he flew between the speeding train and the dingy tunnel walls, pausing only to wink at an astonished Lois Lane as he flew past her window seat.

Superman sped down the subway tunnel. When he was well ahead of the train, he stopped and turned to face the oncoming subway. Superman could see that the engineer was completely unconscious and near death. He had to act to save the man as well as the passengers.

The headlights grew larger and larger, bearing down on Superman. Just before the first car reached him, he kicked his foot into the so-called "third rail," the deadly conductor of millions of volts of electricity. Superman drew all of the electrical power into his own superhuman body, causing a short in the entire system and stopping the train.

Carefully, Superman drew the subway through the darkened tunnel to the next station. The passengers shuffled off in confusion. Superman went to the front of train, taking the unconscious engineer from his cab. To the surprise of the rescue squad, he said, "I'll take this man to the hospital." Cradling him gently in his arms, he lifted him into the air, and flew him to safety.

Lois watched from where she sat in the still, darkened train. Her heart leaped. "Superman," she said. "Thank you."

She waved to him, but he was gone.

Chapter 3

The hot Florida sun beat down on the chain gang shoveling debris from the swampy ooze near a two-lane blacktop road.

Two federal marshals leaned against a beat-up truck parked on the shoulder of the road. It was their job to oversee the monotonous labor and bring the prisoners back at the end of the day. One marshal cleaned his nails with a wooden matchstick. The other dozed. There wasn't anyplace for the prisoners to go anyway.

In chorus, the chain gang wailed a sad song about the troubles of life outside the penitentiary. Singing together broke the monotony of their job. Singing together made the work easier. Singing together —

But they weren't all singing together.

"What is that God-awful noise you're makin'?" one of the prisoner's drawled.

"Mozart!" answered the man at the end of the chain. "Even this wretched pit can't diminish the spirit of true genius! While you've been bending your back in this foul slime, I've been inspired! Life itself began in a murky pool much like this. And a genius such as myself learns to seize the moment. You, my low-forehead friend, are the first to know that I, Lex Luthor, now have a plan to recreate life itself!"

His fellow-prisoner gazed at Lex in total confusion, having understood nothing of what was just said.

"You better be breaking a sweat, Luthor, or we'll feed you to the 'gators!" the marshal called, looking up from his fingernails.

The other marshall opened his eyes. "Hey, Luthor, let's get those duds dirty!" he said.

Lex, his enthusiasm for his own genius undiminished by his environment, shook his head and gazed at the sky. "Surrounded by Neanderthals," he said sadly. He handed a shovel to the man in front of him in the chain gang and returned to his musings about the swamp, keenly aware of the approaching cloud of dust on the road.

A few minutes later, a white convertible screeched to a halt near the truck. The marshals sat up in surprise and watched while the driver emerged. He was a young man, dressed in black leather pants with silver studs and a bright blue Hawaiian shirt. His hair was slicked with grease, drawn up and back into a DA. He was followed out of the car by the loud sound of heavy metal music.

The marshals exchanged glances and waited.

"Yo, Pops," the kid said to the marshal, apparently unaware of the chain gang. "Where on Earth is this and how do I get to Fort Lauderdale?"

"Son, you're on the wrong side of the state," smirked the marshal. He walked over to the car and ran his finger along the hood. "Now that's what I call wheels."

The second marshal joined him. The chain gang watched.

"I guess you yo-yo's have never seen a car like this," the kid said in a superior tone. The look on the marshals' face answered the question. The kid shrugged, and then he smiled magnanimously. "Go on, get in," he invited them, opening the door. "Just feel the leather."

It was completely irresistible. The marshals hopped into the car, as excited as little children on their first train ride. The kid closed the door securely and watched the marshals get the feel of the car, the controls, the steering wheel, the seats. They were too excited with their new toy to notice the kid pull a remote control device out of his pocket and activate it.

In seconds, the top rolled up, the locks clicked shut, and the engine turned over. With a start, the marshals realized they were moving! The kid manipulated the controls, sending the car down the road at forty, fifty, sixty, now eighty miles an hour. Then, as it reached a bridge that spanned the swamp, the kid jerked the control, sending the convertible into the air. And then into the swamp. Forever.

The kid stepped around the old truck and scanned the chain gang.

"Did I do okay, Uncle Lex?" he asked.

"Lenny," Lex said. "I've always thought of you as the Dutch elm disease of my family tree. But this time, Nephew, you did fine."

Smiling with pride for a job well done, Lenny took a large wire clipper from his pocket and freed his uncle from the chain gang.

"Hey, how about giving us a break, Mr. Mozart?" one of the convicts called out.

Lex looked at the man in total shock. "Just because I use my genius in criminal ways doesn't mean I'm not a firm believer in law and order." He sniffed. "You belong in prison!"

The Luthor duo turned on their heels and headed for the old blue truck — and freedom. Lex climbed in the cab.

"Are we going to skip the country, Uncle Lex?" Lenny asked.

"Lenny, your uncle Lex has had only one thing on his awesome mind during his incarceration!"

"What's that, Uncle Lex?" asked Lenny, shorting the ignition in the truck and bringing the engine to life, coughing and sputtering. He got behind the wheel.

"Destroying Superman!" Lex said.

The truck lurched away from the swamp.

Chapter 4

Clark Kent stepped off the elevator in the *Daily Planet* building to — silence. He looked at the deserted office in confusion.

"You're late, Kent!" It was the familiar growl of Perry White, emanating from the conference room.

Clark rushed to follow the voice and began talking before he entered.

"Right, sir," he began. "I promise it won't happen again." He stepped into the conference room and was suddenly facing nearly the entire staff of the *Daily Planet*.

"Ha!" Perry said. The gruff editor in chief sat at the head of the conference table, flanked by Lois Lane and Jimmy Olsen (aspiring young staff photographer for the paper). Near them, and behind Perry, stood the other reporters, editors, and staff.

At the opposite end of the table were two

people, a silver-haired man in a seven-hundred-dollar suit, and a smashingly beautiful young woman who looked as if she'd just stepped off the pages of *Vogue* — dressed for success, and then some.

Clark sidled over to Lois.

"What's everybody doing here?" he whispered.

"Allow me," she said, pointing to the strange man. "The silver fox is none other than Mr. David Warfield."

Clark's mind raced. "You mean that tycoon who owns all those sleazy tabloids that used to be good newspapers?" Clark and every other responsible reporter in the business were saddened every time they saw a good newspaper become irresponsible just so it could have more readers. Good newspapers found their news stories and wrote about them. Sleazy newspapers made the stories up and wrote about them.

"Correction, Clark," Lois said. "Warfield owns 'all those sleazy tabloids,' *and* the *Daily Planet*."

While Clark considered the implications of that news, he watched and listened.

"And, Mr. White," Warfield said, "I have been reading the ledger of this newspaper. The *Daily Planet* hasn't made money in three years!"

"And the name of the game is making money," the beautiful woman who sat beside him said smartly.

17

"Ladies and gentlemen, my daughter, Lacy Warfield," the old man said, introducing the beautiful woman to the staff.

Clark stepped forward and offered his hand. "Uh, nice to make your acquaintance," he said. Lacy stared at him in shock. He withdrew his hand, pushed his glasses back up on his nose, and stepped back.

Lois leaned over to Clark and explained the facts of life to him. "She made *her* money the old-fashioned way. She inherited it." Clark nodded in understanding.

"Lacy will be helping you, Mr. White," Warfield was saying.

"Helping *me*?" Perry said, aghast.

Lacy ignored him. "Once upon a time, the *Daily Planet* was a nice paper," she said. "Now it's just tired. I've had a new layout designed." She reached into a portfolio and brought it out.

She held in her hand a tabloid paper, half the size of the old *Daily Planet*. The top half of the front page was a headline, reading:

SUMMIT KAPUT!
IS WORLD AT BRINK?

The bottom half was a photograph of a bikini-clad model. Her hands were clasped in prayer — presumably she was preparing for the destruction of the world. Clark thought she ought to be wearing more clothes.

"Sir," he spoke to Warfield. "The world isn't

really at the brink. Isn't that headline a bit irresponsible?"

"Maybe," Warfield said with unaccustomed honesty. "But it's a heck of a circulation-booster!"

Perry White's face went from pale to pink to red and was nearing a deep purple when Clark spoke to him.

"Mr. White, don't do anything rash," he advised.

But Perry was beyond calming. "*Rash*?!" he sputtered. "There's the rash that infects world journalism!" He pointed to Warfield. "If you think I'm going to let you — "

"Mr. White," Lacy spoke. "Perhaps I should remind you that Daddy holds your contracts and you must honor them."

Perry couldn't speak anymore. He stormed out of the conference room. Warfield marched out triumphantly. One by one, most of the *Daily Planet* staff left as well.

Politely, but firmly, Clark approached Lacy. "Excuse me, Miss Warfield. I think I speak for all of us when I say we'll do our best to cooperate." He flashed a warning look at Lois before she could disagree with him. "But a reporter's first allegiance is to the truth. The people in this city depend on us. And we can't let them down! Thank you." He reached for Lacy's hand and shook it before making a hasty departure from the conference room.

"Is he for *real*?" Lacy said out loud.

Lois, still standing nearby, smiled sagely.

"One hundred percent. And I like him that way."

"You have a thing for him?" Lacy asked cautiously.

The thought had never seriously crossed Lois's mind. "Clark?" she asked in surprise.

Lacy stared thoughtfully at the door through which Clark had just walked. "I think he's kind of cute," she said.

Lois took another look at Lacy. She couldn't picture Lacy and Clark as an item. "Forget it, Princess," she laughed. "Clark is the world's oldest Boy Scout. He's trustworthy, loyal, obedient, helpful, and a friend to every other scout," she recited. "And I promise, he's not interested in anyone like *you*."

"But all men like me, Lois. I'm very rich."

"And very foolish," Lois finished for her. But inside, deep inside, there was a little part of Lois that wondered if sweet, square Clark Kent would be able to resist the temptations of Lacy Warfield.

Chapter 5

"Lois! Get in here!" Perry White bellowed from his office.

Lois and Lacy went into the office together. Clark and Mr. Warfield were already there. Perry's television was turned on, and the screen showed a close-up of the President of the United States. He was speaking in serious tones, his face lined with worry.

"The President is speaking," Clark said to Lois. "I don't think it's going to be good news."

"You always overreact, Clark. How terrible can it be?"

"Hopefully *very* terrible," Mr. Warfield said, barging in on their conversation. "We can double our circulation with a good international crisis."

Lois and Clark looked at him in shock. Was it possible that somebody could welcome an international crisis just because it might make him rich? The grim smile on Warfield's face told them it was true.

"Isn't that wonderful?" Perry said sarcastically.

In another part of America — as far from Metropolis as Clark's hometown of Smallville — the students in an eighth-grade classroom were watching the same broadcast of the President as the *Daily Planet* staff saw in Perry White's office.

". . . and because the Summit has failed, we have no choice but to strive to be second to none in the nuclear arms race." The President laid the papers on his desk and looked solemnly at the camera. Each student felt the seriousness of his words and the burden of his worry. And they felt totally helpless. The television clicked off.

"I know you're all upset by the crisis. The best thing we can do is try to think positively. Is there anything we can do?" their teacher asked. "Should we write to our congressman?"

There was no response. The teacher's eyes moved around the room. She was hoping for a sign of optimism. In ground where there was hope, anything could grow. But all she saw were glum, worried faces. Except for one. Jeremy, the class dreamer, was drawing something on the paper in front of him. At first, she thought he wasn't paying attention, but then she glanced at the picture, instantly recognizing Superman's likeness by his blue outfit and red cape.

"Jeremy," she said. "Do you have a suggestion?"

"I don't want to write to my congressman. I'm going to write a letter to Superman!"

At first, there was a stunned silence in the class. Then there were a few smirking giggles.

"Look, Superman is the one guy who could pull it off," Jeremy told his classmates. "No one would mess with him. He'll collect all the bombs. Zap!! They're history."

A lot of the kids were laughing now. They couldn't believe Jeremy thought Superman would pay attention to anything a kid told him — and they were already too wise in the wicked ways of the world to believe that anybody else had a way to stop the nuclear madness, either.

Jeremy was angry, though. "You all think you're so cool, right? Well, you'll be cooler when the whole world gets vaporized, and you didn't do anything to stop it. Well, I'm going to write Superman a letter and send it to the *Daily Planet*!"

And then, he took a fresh piece of paper and a sharp pencil and began his letter, oblivious of the continued smirks around him.

Chapter 6

At the same moment Jeremy was thinking about Superman, someone else was thinking about him as well. But he wasn't thinking about how Superman could save the world from destruction. He was thinking about how he could destroy Superman. It was Lex Luthor.

Lex and Lenny had joined a tour of the Metropolis Museum and listened while the guide came to the part they had been waiting for.

"This is our newest and most popular exhibit," she said. She pointed to a forty-foot-tall statue of Superman. It was surrounded by cases full of memorabilia, photographs, letters, facts, and figures about the Man of Steel.

And then there was a globe of Earth, seemingly suspended by a tiny black wire.

"Superman has graciously donated a strand of his hair to the museum," the guide said, pointing to the tiny black "wire." "So we all could have the fun of seeing how strong he really is. Here, you can see a one-thousand-pound globe easily suspended by his single hair!" The crowd gaped at the exhibit and then, at the suggestion of the guide, moved on to the next exhibit.

Except for Lex and Lenny. They waited patiently while the rest of the group shuffled off to Primates. As the last footfall echoed away, Lex yanked off the hat and sunglasses that had served as a disguise. He bowed regally to the forty-foot statue.

"Guess who!" he said, revealing himself. "It's me, your old buddy, Lex Luthor. Say, you don't look too bad yourself. Of course, I've put on a few pounds, but what the hay! They feed you a lot of starchy foods when you're in *prison*. That's p-r-i-s-o-n, as in where you put me, Mr. Clean. Say, we should get together soon. Over lunch, over dinner, or" — he paused for effect — "over your dead body." Lex laughed wickedly at his demented joke and then turned to his nephew. "Do you realize what I can create with a single strand of Superman's hair?"

Lenny put his mind to the question. His fondest wish was once, just once, to be as smart as his uncle. He thought he had the answer this time: "A toupee that flies?" he asked brightly.

Lex sighed. "I look at you, Lenny, and I know how the Romans felt when the barbarians arrived at their city gate. Superman's hair contains a sample of Superman's genetic material. The building blocks of his body. With my genius and enough nuclear power to mutate those genes, I will create a being with all his powers — but with absolute allegiance to me!"

Lex nodded, giving Lenny the go-ahead sign.

Lenny removed a large iron mallet from his oversize coat pocket. He swung the mallet back over his head and brought it forward and down onto the display case, smashing the glass to smithereens.

Lenny stood back from the shattered case and began dropping smoke bombs around the exhibit, shrouding himself and his uncle until their dastardly deed was done.

Lex reached into the iron globe display, quickly unknotted the strand of Superman's hair, and pocketed it.

"Happy trails, Blue Boy!" he said suavely. "Until we meet again."

Laughing wickedly at his own cleverness, he and Lenny left the scene of the crime.

Chapter 7

Lacy Warfield was making her pitch to Clark Kent — in more ways than one.

She had called him into her office to talk about a series she wanted him to do. When he arrived, she was sitting on her desk, long silky legs dangling alluringly toward him. As ever, she was dressed in expensive clothes that showed everything to her best advantage. Clark, apparently, saw none of it.

"You wanted me, Miss Warfield?" he asked.

"Oh, *yes*," she said, and then realized that she and Clark were speaking about different things. "Yes, Clark, but please call me Lacy." Clark nodded. "Listen, we've got a brilliant idea for a series. Daddy thinks it's brilliant, too. We'll do the research together and you'll write it. It's called 'Metropolis After Hours.' We'll go to all of the city's hot night spots and discos. We'll go to restaurants and night clubs. We'll go to — "

"Uh, Lacy," Clark interrupted. "I really don't think I — "

"But you're perfect for it. You're young. You're single — "

"And I'm usually in bed by ten-thirty," he finished the sentence for her.

But Lacy wouldn't hear any more protests. Her mind was made up. If the only way she could have a date with Clark Kent was to pretend it was business — well, she'd pretend it was business. In her life, she'd met rich and powerful men, empire builders, magnates. But she'd never met a man who was as fascinating and mysterious to her as Clark Kent. She wanted to find the right word to describe him. Different, she decided, watching him stand near her, bashfully pushing his glasses up onto his nose again. He was simply different from anybody else she'd ever known.

"Don't worry, Clark. You won't be alone. I know all the right places in this town. We start tonight at the grand opening of the Metro Club. It's a date!" she said triumphantly.

Clark gulped, but before he could object, Lois appeared at Lacy's office door with a letter in her hand.

"A date?" she teased.

Clark nodded. "It's just research, actually."

Lois ignored Clark's embarrassed discomfort. "This letter was addressed to Superman care of me," she told Lacy.

"Superman gets mail here?" Lacy asked in surprise.

"Oh, it's probably just a picture request," Clark said. "I'll take care of it if you want, Lois." He reached for the letter, knowing it was the fastest way for Superman to get his mail.

"This isn't exactly a fan letter," Lois said. "You read it, Clark," she said, handing it to him.

Clark's eyes scanned Jeremy's letter instantly. He was shaken by what he read. While Lois and Lacy waited, he collected his feelings and read out loud to them.

". . . Once you've destroyed all the nuclear missiles in the world, nobody will laugh at me anymore. They'll see that I was right. Superman *can* make sure that we don't blow ourselves up. Quick and easy. Thanks a lot. I know you'll come through. Your friend, Jeremy."

"Poor kid," Lois said. "Oh, well, back to work." She left Lacy's office.

But Clark didn't hear her, and neither did Lacy.

"What an angle!" Lacy said, to nobody in particular. "Daddy just loves to whip up campaigns! Readers'll eat it up. We're going to make this kid a celebrity. The whole world will be waiting for Superman's answer."

Lacy reached for her telephone and punched in some numbers. "Hold the afternoon editions!" she shouted into the instrument and then slammed it back down. "Daddy will be so proud of me!" she preened.

Clark was only vaguely aware of Lacy's ravings. She was thinking about the paper, but he was thinking about Jeremy, whose friends laughed at him because he had written a letter to Superman.

Perhaps it was true that Superman could save the world, but at that moment, he was more concerned about saving Jeremy.

Chapter 8

Jeremy sat in his classroom, gazing out the window and daydreaming. It was his favorite thing to do. When he looked through that window, he could see anything he wanted. Just then, for instance, he saw the school's playground, where children played happily and nobody laughed at him; and the town beyond, where people lived peacefully and they cared about him. He could see. . . .

Superman!

Jeremy leaped out of his seat in surprise.

"Jeremy, do you have a question?" his teacher asked.

"No, I just saw Superman!" His classmates laughed. "I really did," he said. "Right outside the window." But when he looked again, there wasn't a sign of Superman. And the laughter continued.

"I must have been daydreaming," he said sadly, sitting down again. It was one thing when his classmates made a fool of him. It was another thing when he did it to himself.

And then there was a knock at the classroom door. Everyone turned and watched as Superman, himself, came into the classroom, carrying Jeremy's letter. Jeremy was astonished, and all of his friends and their teacher were speechless.

"I'm sorry to interrupt your lesson," Superman said to Jeremy's teacher. "But I wanted to answer Jeremy in person."

Everybody turned to look at Jeremy. Where, only a few minutes ago, there had been smirks and giggles about Jeremy, now there was total admiration and awe. Jeremy glowed with pride as Superman walked over to him.

"Jeremy, this is the most important letter I've ever received. But I'm afraid what you're asking me to do is impossible."

As suddenly as they had been born, Jeremy's hopes were dashed. He couldn't believe that anything would be impossible for Superman.

"Impossible? Why?" Jeremy asked.

"Because I made a vow. I promised my father that I would never interfere with the destiny of your planet."

If Jeremy was hearing this right, Superman had just told him that even though he could do things to save Earth from its own destruction, he wasn't going to. He'd stand by and just watch the world come to an end.

"What good is your vow going to do if we

just blow ourselves away? What good was my letter?"

"Your letter made me understand that I have a responsibility to share your concern with the leaders of the world. I promise you they will hear it. It is their job to represent the people of Earth and to stop the nuclear insanity."

The entire class was silent, stunned. The teacher sensed their discomfort. Superman was aware, too, that his answer to Jeremy hadn't really satisfied the boy. Jeremy had been so certain that Superman could solve everything that he couldn't understand why he might not do something that was within his power. But Superman knew that the temptation was there. Power was nearly irresistible — even for superhumans.

Jor-El's words from so long ago rang in Superman's ears: "It is forbidden for you to interfere in Earth's history. It is forbidden. . . . It is forbidden. . . ." The words echoed in his memory.

"I'm sure we all want to thank Superman for taking the time to visit us," Jeremy's teacher said to the class, and then she spoke to Superman. "Thank you. We understand."

"Well, *I* don't understand!" Jeremy said angrily.

"I'm sorry" was all Superman could say to Jeremy, and he knew it wouldn't help at all. Disheartened, but still sure he was doing the right thing, he left the classroom.

"Told you so!" one of Jeremy's classmates whined at him.

Jeremy wondered what good Superman was if he couldn't help when Earth needed him the most.

Chapter 9

Meanwhile, in Metropolis, there was evil brewing.

Lex Luthor sat at the computer controls in his lair. He had moved his headquarters from the underground palace in the railroad station. Now, he lived and worked in a skytop apartment forty stories above the city in Metropolis Tower.

The interior had geometrically patterned marble floors in the main room, which was a two-story split-level octagon. It was completely surrounded by windows with ornate geometric designs in the glass. Beyond the windows, the entire apartment was encircled by a terrace, which afforded a panoramic view of all of Metropolis.

At that moment, however, Lex Luthor was unaware of his surroundings. All of his considerable intellect was focused on a single task: destroying Superman.

Lex flipped a few final switches at the control panel, checked the digital read-out, and monitored the heat calibrations on the screen. Then he waited, and watched.

In the lab, which could be seen through thermal glass, there stood a nuclear chamber, completely under the control of the computer. The chamber was similar to a telephone booth with a translucent glass door. While the experiment continued, multicolored lights emitted from the nuclear chamber, flashing through its door. The reaction within the chamber caused trails of steam to rise around its outside.

Lex Luthor's face glowed with joy. He sensed a success beyond his own expectations.

"I am smarter than even I thought. It's working!" Then he turned to his nephew, who seemed unaware of the activities. "Quick, Lenny. Prepare the nuclear chamber!" There was no answer. No response. "Lenny?" he asked. "Lenny!" he yelled.

Lenny was oblivious of his uncle's wishes. The earphones wrapped around his head told the story. While he listened to music from a pocket tape deck, he kept time with two drumsticks. As far as he was concerned, his uncle was in another world.

Lex stepped over to Lenny, flicked off his earphones, and yelled into his ear to get his attention. "LEONARD!" It got his attention. "Get the radiation suits!"

Lenny dropped the drumsticks and fetched

white radiation suits, which they donned quickly. Lex fiddled with the controls at the computer panel, lowering the lights in the room until the only light was the glow from the nuclear chamber.

Then, carefully, ever so carefully, Lex began the final phase of his experiment. He brought the embryonic genetic material to the nuclear chamber. The protoplasm was housed in a protective dish. Lex locked the protoplasm into the chamber and left the lab, shutting the steel doors behind him. While Lex and Lenny watched through the glass, the protoplasm seemed to grow and spread formlessly, a gelatinous mass. If Lex's calculations were correct, the mass was about to take a new — and deadly — form.

In an expansive mood, Lex explained his theory to Lenny. "Every day the earth is bombarded by radioactive cosmic rays. Over millions of years, the radiation made single cells evolve into . . . us." He paused, briefly, as if wanting to double-check that he and Lenny were part of the same evolution. "Now, Leonard, your Uncle Lex, using this protoplasm I've grown from Superman's cells, will duplicate Creation itself in a matter of seconds!"

Lenny was awestruck. Lex turned back to the control panel and began executing a series of computer commands. The reaction began. Lights flashed, and there was a rumbling sound that built slowly to a roar, which, finally, sounded like a human scream. A gigantic humanoid shadow struck the translucent door of the chamber. Silhouetted arms rose in protest, and the roaring scream came again.

"It's . . . alive!" Lex shouted with joy, reaching to punch open the lock on the chamber door and the laboratory door. "Now, watch, Lenny. See how he obeys my commands." The steel door to the laboratory slid open. "Come on down, big boy!" he invited.

Unfortunately, Lenny couldn't watch. He was hiding, in terror, behind his uncle.

But the results of the experiment didn't use the open doors. It crashed through the walls of the chamber and the laboratory, spreading debris all over Lex's apartment. It didn't matter to Lex. Nothing mattered to Lex except that his experiment had succeeded. Through the smoke, steam, and dust, he could hear heavy and steady footsteps, which meant only one thing. Success.

Then, the dust settled. There, in front of Lex and Lenny stood the transformed protoplasm. It was a monstrous humanoid creature. Rippling muscles attested to its strength. Lex's fondest wish was being realized right before his eyes.

Then the creature's mouth opened. Sound began to form. He reached out to Lex and, in his booming roar, uttered his first word.

"F-f-f-f-faaaaaaather!"

Chapter 10

Lex gazed with the pride of a first-time father on his newborn monster.

"He needs something to wear, Uncle Lex," Lenny said.

Lex handed him a pair of coveralls, and when he had put them on, he handed the creature a solid-iron ingot.

"Now break it!" he ordered. It was a test that the creature passed with flying colors, snapping the ingot in two easily. Lex let out his breath. "He has all of Superman's powers — if I've planned it right." Lex reached for a nearby machine gun and aimed it at his creation. "Stand back, Lenny," he warned, and then released a volley of bullets at the creature. They bounced off him harmlessly.

"Now for the final test. Can he fly? I command you to rise!"

Without warning, the creature shot up into the air, or, more accurately, into the ceiling.

He plummeted into a heap on the floor. Lex and Lenny ran to his aid.

"Okay, okay, so he needs a little coaching," Lex reasoned, helping the creature to a chair. Then, an idea occurred to Lex. It would be wise for Metropolis to have a little look at his creation — to be prepared for the inevitable confrontation of the world's superpowers — Superman vs. Nuclear Man.

Lex thumbed through the *Daily Planet*, shaking his head sadly at the "new" Warfield format. "I don't know what this country's coming to. This used to be a fine paper," he grumbled. But he kept looking. "Aha, here!" he announced.

Lenny looked at the headline that had caught Lex's attention:

GRAND OPENING OF CHIC NIGHT SPOT TONIGHT!

"Gee, Uncle Lex, I don't think this guy's much of a dancer."

Lex gave him a withering look. "Let's try to keep your I.Q. a family secret, Leonard. Before we launch him against Superman, we have to test him. See how well he does with mayhem and destruction."

Lex stood up and walked over to Nuclear Man, picking up his Superman Dartboard on the way. "I created you for one reason only," he said, pulling the darts from the bulls-eye on the board for clearer demonstration. "To destroy this man!"

Nuclear Man's face lit up with the joy of understanding. His mouth opened tortuously and he spoke for the second time in his life. "Yes . . . F-f-faaather!"

That night, a reluctant Clark Kent and an eager Lacy Warfield arrived at the wild party celebrating the opening of The Metro Club — the very event Nuclear Man was scheduled to attend as an uninvited guest.

Lacy drew Clark to the head of the very long line waiting outside the club. Two huge men, the club's "bouncers" barred the door, keeping a young couple from entering.

"See, it's our honeymoon, and we just wanted to have one dance here — "

" — so I can tell everyone back home. Please? Please!" The bouncers turned a deaf ear to their request, spotting Lacy and Clark. "Good evening, Miss Warfield," one said warmly, allowing them into the club. Clark followed Lacy in. He felt bad about being in a place he didn't want to be while that eager young couple tried unsuccessfully to beg their way in.

The interior of the club was lit with sparkling colored lights that danced off the floor and ceiling. The overwhelming sensation, though, was noise, for music blared from every corner, and people danced in a frenzy on the crowded floor.

"I've never been in a place like this before!" Clark told Lacy.

"This is Metropolis after hours! This is what

you'll be writing about. C'mon, let's dance."

Clark joined her on the dance floor, and at once began bumping into everyone around him — or they were bumping into him. It was impossible to tell which. Clark politely said "Excuse me," to each bump until a well-dressed young man cut in on him, asking Lacy to dance.

Clark excused himself from the dance floor, his mind still on the helpless young couple outside. Moving so fast that nobody could even see him, he rushed outside, picked up the young couple, and brought them inside. The bouncers only felt a brief rush of air pass them. The next thing the honeymooners knew, they were standing together on the dance floor, too astonished to move.

"I believe you're supposed to dance," Clark said.

They did.

Chapter 11

Clark spotted Lacy on the dance floor and angled through the crowd to reach her.

"Remember me?" he asked. Her glowing smile was her answer.

The music slowed to a romantic number. Clark took her right hand in his left, and put her left hand on his shoulder. They danced the old-fashioned way.

"Don't tell me. You learned to dance at church socials," she said.

"Actually, I had a crash course from my mother the night before my prom."

Lacy smiled. That was almost exactly what she expected Clark to say. He was so wholesome, so kind, so different from anyone she'd ever known before. She liked him. She began to think that perhaps his values were better than the ones her father had taught her.

"I bet you have some freckle-faced girl waiting for you in Smallville," she said.

"Oh, no, there's no one back home, or here for that matter."

That was just what Lacy was hoping to hear. Content, she danced with Clark, oblivious to the noise and the crowd and the arrival of Nuclear Man.

Nuclear Man swept past the bouncers and into the club. He was immediately dazzled by the lights and began bumping into the customers. One man, infuriated because Nuclear Man made him spill his drinks, took a swing at the monster. Nuclear Man caught the oncoming fist with his hand and crushed the man's knuckles.

He continued his march forward until he stood on the edge of the dance floor, watching the gyrations. And then he saw Lacy and Clark.

His eyes were transfixed by the beautiful Lacy Warfield. It was as if he had been waiting all of his very short life for this one moment — this one experience. To him then, nothing mattered but Lacy. He was in love with her!

At just that moment, an older woman spotted the very confused Nuclear Man. In the dim and flashing light, she thought him as handsome as he thought Lacy beautiful. She took him by the hand and led him out the back door of the Metro Club. Dumbstruck, he followed her. But as soon as the woman saw Nuclear Man in the bright streetlights, she knew she'd made a terrible mistake.

She did the only logical thing. She screamed!

Inside the club, still on the dance floor with Lacy, Clark heard the woman's wail of distress.

"Excuse me, Lacy," Clark said. "There's something I must do — "

While Lacy watched in surprise, Clark ran off the dance floor toward the men's room, removing his glasses as he ran.

Clark Kent was done for the night. Now, it was Superman's turn!

Chapter 12

Superman sped to the still-screaming woman in the alley. She screamed a final time as she ran past him to safety, leaving him alone to face his genetically designed arch-enemy.

Nuclear Man was ready for him. He stood at the far end of the alley near the parking lot, poised for action. As Superman approached, Nuclear Man lifted a huge garbage Dumpster and lofted it toward Superman. It caught him unawares, knocking him to the ground — but not for long.

Superman leaped toward his foe, who fled down another alley. As soon as Superman rounded the corner, he was met with a powerful punch. Nuclear Man had been waiting for him. Superman was thrown against a truck, but he recovered and attacked again, this time drawing Nuclear Man out into the relative open of the parking lot.

Nuclear Man lunged at Superman, nearly

knocking him to the ground. Superman regained his balance and attacked Nuclear Man, this time throwing him against a fence.

The battle raged on, the two opponents almost equal. They traded punches and kicks, neither winning, neither losing.

Superman lunged to attack Nuclear Man for what he hoped would be a final time. Desperate to obey his "father," Lex Luthor, and destroy Superman, Nuclear Man grasped a lamppost and tore it out of the pavement. He raised it up over his head and brought it down on Superman with all of his force.

Superman saw it coming. He was ready. As the end of the lamppost reached him, he grabbed it, halting its downward movement. He wrested it from Nuclear Man, took it in both hands, and swung it round. As he came full circle, the lamppost whacked Nuclear Man in his midsection with such force that it lifted him up out of the parking lot and sent him sailing off into the night.

"Home run!" Superman shouted triumphantly, and then flew after Nuclear Man to watch the grand finale.

And what a grand finale it was! The flying body of Nuclear Man struck Metropolis's largest electrical transformer, showering sparks high into the midnight sky. Never had Metropolis seen such a pyrotechnic display!

Superman watched the final destruction of Nuclear Man. When all that was left was a quivering mass of protoplasm, Superman turned his attention to repairing the transformer. Unless he repaired the damage, Metropolis would suffer a terrible blackout. He worked quickly, concentrating on his task.

He didn't see the man in the shadows, watching sadly. It was Lenny. Lenny emerged from the darkness and stepped over to Nuclear Man's remains. He scooped them into a plastic bag and left silently. Superman finished his work and left.

Later that night, Lenny returned to Lex's laboratory and displayed the last traces of Lex's failed experiment to his uncle.

"Superman broke your monster, Uncle Lex!" Lenny wailed unhappily.

"I must have miscalculated!" Lex said thoughtfully. "How . . . ?"

He scratched his bald head and mused aloud. "Obviously normal radiation doesn't generate enough mutant power in the cells. I need a greater source of energy. If only I could bake the genetic material in the core of the sun!" He shook his head in dismay. "Impossible. Even I have no way to reach the sun."

"Poor Uncle Lex," Lenny said sympathetically.

Chapter 13

David Warfield's limousine drove regally through the city toward the airport. Father and daughter sat in the back, a rare chance for a family reunion.

Warfield patted his daughter's hand and smiled with pride. "Bringing the kid here who wrote the letter to Superman will be our greatest publicity gimmick. And it was your idea! Perhaps it's time to discuss giving you a free reign at one of my papers" — he paused for effect — "Miss Publisher."

But it had no effect. Lacy's mind was on something else. "Clark Kent," she muttered. "Who does he think he is! He never even said good-night!"

"Clark Kent!" her father said. "You were going out with a reporter?" He said the last word as if it were a dirty handkerchief.

"Oh, no," Lacy protested. "We went dancing — for a story he's writing." Her answer even sounded lame to Lacy.

"Your grandfather had one iron rule that's stood me well," Warfield lectured Lacy. "Never fraternize with the help. Keep to your own station! Am I clear?"

Lacy nodded. Her father was right. It made sense to keep to her own station. The real question was, What exactly was her station?

She didn't have time to think about that now, though. As they pulled into the airport, the private jet carrying Jeremy was landing.

Warfield hopped out of the limousine and escorted the young boy to the crowd of eager reporters and photographers. "Go ahead, son," Warfield spoke to Jeremy. "Tell the American public what you told me."

Jeremy was totally awed by the attention. He couldn't believe that he was in Metropolis, and the center of everybody's attention, just because he had written a letter to Superman. Warfield nudged him, reminding him he had a question to answer.

"I just said . . ." But he couldn't think what he wanted to say. Camera flashes erupted all around him. Warfield put his arm around the boy's shoulder. It gave him some strength. "I just said, I wish Superman had said 'yes.' "

The afternoon edition of the *Daily Planet* hit Perry White's desk. There was a picture of Jeremy at the airport. The headline read:

SUPERMAN TO KID: DROP DEAD!

"I'm through taking it lying down!" Perry roared. He stormed out of his office, still shouting. "If anybody wants me, I'll be downtown!" Then, he was gone.

Puzzled, Jimmy turned to Lois. "Did the Chief look different to you?" he asked.

"Yeah," she said. "He looked like my dad did every time he went to the bank to try and borrow money."

Clark stood near them, staring balefully at the headline.

"Clark, there's nothing any of us can do. It's Superman's decision. I'm sure he knows what he's doing."

Clark wished Superman were so sure. Deeply concerned — about Jeremy, about the *Daily Planet*, about the world — he wandered out of the office and into the hallway.

He was just in time to run into the Warfield contingent, escorting Jeremy to more fame. Clark could tell that Jeremy was bewildered by what was happening to him. Somehow, right and wrong were getting confused in Jeremy's world.

When Jeremy saw Clark Kent, he saw a familiar, calm reassurance about the man.

"Do I know you?" he asked.

Superman knew Jeremy, but Clark Kent did not. He introduced himself.

"Do you know Superman?" Jeremy whispered to him.

Clark pushed his glasses back up onto his nose. He nodded. "Is there something you want me to tell him for you?" he asked.

Jeremy nodded. "Just tell him I didn't mean to cause him trouble. Tell him not to listen to what all these papers are saying. I just want him to do what he thinks is right."

"Don't worry," Clark told the boy. "I'm sure Superman cares a lot more about what is in one boy's heart than he does about all the editorials in Warfield Publications."

And Clark knew that was true.

Chapter 14

In a flash of red and blue, Superman left the airspace over Metropolis. He had a decision to make, and it wasn't an easy one. When times were tough like this, he had but one place to go — his Fortress of Solitude.

Situated in the vast Arctic expanse, not far from the magnetic North Pole, the Fortress of Solitude offered him a world of his own. It had been constructed from the green Kryptonian crystal that had traveled with Superman from his home planet.

Superman stood at the base of icy peaks, hands on his hips, surveying the landscape. When he was sure, he stamped on the frozen tundra. As if in response to his thunderous pounding, the snow began to shake loose from the mountains — an avalanche — revealing the Fortress.

Superman stepped in. He went straight to the crystals of knowledge, a Kryptonian "library," selected one of the clear crystals, and slipped it into the "reader."

Once again, Superman viewed the horrible fate of his own planet. Krypton had exploded and disintegrated in a great conflagration. Superman's own parents, Jor-El and Lara, had known it would happen, but were unable to convince the elders of Krypton to evacuate the planet. If only Jor-El had refused to keep silent, perhaps the people of the planet might have been saved. Perhaps they would be alive today, Superman thought.

Perhaps it was now that *he* had to speak, where his father had kept silent. Perhaps he had to act as his father had not.

"I know I have been forbidden to act, but now Earth awaits a fate as terrible as Krypton's!" he cried to the ages.

As if the crystals from Krypton had heard him, they reminded him of his terrible oath.

"Earth is too primitive," one voice said. "You can flee to new worlds where war is long forgotten."

A second voice chimed in. "If you teach the people of the world to put their fate in the hands of any one man — even yourself — you are teaching them to be betrayed!"

Superman listened, and he heard, but he knew that, wise as those men were, they were wrong. His mind was made up. He spoke again. "You have taught me well, but sometimes there is more to learn from children than the wisest of men."

He was ready to go back to Metropolis now. He lifted himself into the sky and flew south. As he left, the snow camouflage was drawn back onto the spires of the Fortress of Solitude. When Superman glanced back over his shoulder, it was as if he'd never been there at all.

Lacy and Lois sat across a small table from one another at a sidewalk café in Metropolis. Lacy fingered the top of the straw that stuck out from her frosty drink. Her mind wandered.

Lois sat forward in her chair and spoke intensely, unaware that Lacy wasn't listening.

"The notion that your father would stoop low enough to attack Superman just to sell more papers. . . ."

"I know I'm not exactly a Girl Scout, but, maybe if I show him I'm trying, he'll like me."

Lois was confused by this response. "Who?" she asked.

"Clark. He's late again. I can't figure him out."

"That's because there's nothing to figure out. Now will you please pay attention? I'm not through insulting your father!"

"Lois, have you ever fallen for a guy, and he's not like other guys? It's like you come from two different worlds?"

Like Krypton, Lois thought. Yes, she thought

she knew exactly what Lacy meant. Funny that she and Lacy, so totally different from one another, should have something in common. Thinking about her feelings for Superman made Lois forget all about David Warfield.

"And your heart beats faster just thinking about him," Lois said.

"Right, and you want to tell him how you feel — "

"But he's never there," Lois finished her sentence for her.

"Why, Lois!" Lacy said in surprise. "I didn't know. Who is he?"

But before Lois could tell her — as if she would have — there was a crash as a waiter dropped a tray of glasses. Stunned, he pointed upward.

"Look, up in the sky! It's — "

"Superman!" Lois said, knowing in her own heart that she'd answered Lacy's question.

Chapter 15

With super-speed and X-ray vision, Superman scanned all of Metropolis to locate one small boy. In a matter of seconds, he found him.

Jeremy was standing on a street corner with Jimmy Olsen, who was photographing him eating a hot dog. Superman flew down to his side.

"Superman! What a scoop," Jimmy said, stunned, and then he clicked a few pictures of Superman and Jeremy.

"Would you be willing to take a walk with me?" Superman said to the boy.

"Absolutely!" Jeremy told him.

Together, they walked across town, gathering a large and curious crowd as they went. Jimmy followed them, snapping pictures constantly. Superman didn't pause for anything until he and Jeremy arrived at their destination — the United Nations.

At the door to the General Assembly, two guards stopped them, uncertain how to react.

One turned to the other. "I don't think he has a pass," he said.

"I don't think he needs a pass," the other said. The decision made, they opened the doors for Superman and Jeremy, who stepped in.

"Would you mind waiting for me in the visitors' gallery?" Superman asked Jeremy. The boy scooted up the stairs, joining the arriving throng, which included Lois and Lacy. At the same time, Superman strode forward toward the podium. Along the way, the delegates stared in shock as they saw Superman walk through their sanctuary.

When he reached the front, he spoke to the Secretary General, a woman wearing a beautiful blue and gold sari. "Madame Secretary," Superman said. "May I address the delegates?"

Stunned, she nodded and then said, "But you need a sponsor."

Superman turned to look for help from the delegates. He didn't even have to ask. Every single hand was raised for sponsorship.

"I believe that will do," she said, and then offered him the podium.

Slowly, Superman mounted the steps and turned to face the delegates. The General Assembly, he knew, had in it representatives from nearly every country in the world. The faces and clothes he saw represented a vast array of cultures, religions, languages, and nations. But as he looked at them, he knew that they were also united in their hope for peace in the world, and in their excited anticipation of his message.

He stepped forward and spoke: "For many years, I have lived among you as a visitor. I've seen beauty in your many cultures, and I've felt joy in your many accomplishments. But I've also seen the folly of your wars. As of today, I am no longer a visitor." He paused and then went on. "Earth is my home, too. We cannot live in fear. I cannot watch you tumble into the madness of nuclear destruction. So I have come to a decision."

The delegates sat forward in their seats. Superman continued. "I am going to do what your governments have been unable to do. I will rid our planet of all nuclear weapons."

There was a stunned silence.

Then, from the balcony, Jeremy stood up and yelled: "All *right!!!!*"

The delegates joined in along with the rest of the visitors' gallery.

Superman was sure this was the right answer for his home planet, Earth.

Chapter 16

And then, the world watched.

Each of the world's powers had nuclear weapons, hundreds, thousands of them. One by one, Superman located them and destroyed them.

He plunged into oceans, gathering missiles from submarines. He scanned the frozen tundra, finding isolated missile silos. He purged the nations of all arsenals.

He forged a giant net that hung weightlessly in space. As he collected warheads, he stored them in this net and, when it was full, he delivered the deadly payload to the one place in Earth's solar system that it would be totally harmless: the sun.

Superman brought the first load of missiles near to the sun. He took firm hold of the net and began swinging the lethal load around and around until an incredible burst of centrifugal force sent it spinning into the sun's own nuclear furnace.

Great tentacles of fire leaped from the sun's surface; storms of a billion megaton force bubbled in its core. In a matter of seconds, it was over.

Superman returned to Earth to collect more of the missiles.

In the Pentagon, the bureaucratic heart of America's military forces, a group of solemn men — politicians and soldiers — watched Superman's progress. Charts told them each time a missile was removed from their own stores, as well as the stores of others — enemy and ally alike. Activity on the sun allowed them to monitor the ultimate destruction.

"So far, so good," said a senator. "But even for Superman, it will take a long time to dispose of these arsenals."

"Let's just make sure he doesn't leave one side with a few souvenirs — particularly if it's the *other* side."

"I trust Superman," the senator snapped.

"So do I," the general said. "But he's the only one I do trust."

The senator understood then. There was a danger that someone might fool Superman. An imbalance of nuclear weapons was even more dangerous than the standoff they'd had before. Unscrupulous people might. . . . But he couldn't even think about that. He knew that they had to trust Superman.

Superman swept back into the earth's atmosphere and once again began the arduous task of locating and removing the nuclear devices from their hiding places. And each time one was found and taken away, the citizens of Earth cheered.

One in particular felt that Superman's humanitarian activities were cause for celebration: Lex Luthor.

Lex had invited three visitors to his skytop hideaway to join in the celebration — three men whom he needed very much to execute his devilish plan. He had only to convince them that they needed *him*.

The three men eyed one another suspiciously, awaiting Lex's arrival, wondering what was up.

When Lex stepped into the room, each jumped up, producing small revolvers out of personal hiding places. After all, they hadn't gotten where they were by being incautious.

"Nice to see you, too," Lex greeted them warmly. "Now, if we can just relax, I'll get started with the introductions." Reluctantly, each stashed his handgun and sat down at Lex's conference table.

"Now, first, on my right," Lex pointed to a nervous man who was wearing a tweed jacket with leather patches. He had wire-rimmed glasses and a girth that suggested a comfortable life. "From the land of the free and home of the cost overrun, let's welcome Harry Howler, nuclear strategist for America's top think tank and a great warmonger in his own right." Harry nodded, acknowledging the less-than-complimentary introduction. Still, he couldn't — and wouldn't — deny it.

Lex went on, pointing to an impeccably dressed and perfectly groomed silver-haired man sitting on Harry's right. ". . . And next, a hearty *bienvenue* to Jean-Pierre DuBois, nuclear warhead dealer to the world. His motto: 'If you didn't buy it from Jean-Pierre, you didn't buy it on the black market.' " Jean-Pierre blushed to hear it.

"And our third guest"—Lex indicated a bushy-eyebrowed Soviet general in full uniform — "has a bad rap for always trying to drag his country into war. Some people like to call General Romoff the Mad Russian, but to me he's just eccentric."

At that moment, there was a tremendously loud BANG! from somewhere in Lex's apartment. The three guests jumped up nervously, reaching for their weapons once again.

Lex shrugged the incident off. "My nephew, Lenny, is learning the drums," he explained. Then, he began his pitch in earnest. It was the moment the guests had been waiting for. "Look, I know you're all a little choked up right now. You're overcome by the joy of knowing that Superman is ending the arms race!" He paused to let that sink in because, of course, each of them was devastated about Superman's actions — perhaps the only men on the planet who felt that way. "Think of it, DuBois, you can finally *retire*. You can go into something nice like home appliances. There's a real mark-up in dishwashers."

It hurt. It hurt because DuBois knew Lex was right. Without a market for nuclear weapons, he might as well be selling dishwashers. They were all in the same boat. All because of Superman.

Lex knew that he'd hit home. He went on. "The point is that I, Lex Luthor, the greatest criminal mind of the modern era, have discovered a way *to destroy Superman!*"

Chapter 17

At first, after Lex's announcement, there was a stunned silence. Then the quiet disappeared, drowned by a cacophonous drum solo. "Oh, Lenny?" Lex said brightly, still smiling. There was no answer. Lex looked for sympathy: "Any of you guys have teenagers at home?" The three men only stared. *"LENNY!!!"*

Lenny appeared, drumsticks in his hand. Lex took the drumsticks and broke them neatly in two.

"Get the box, Nephew," he said. Lenny high-tailed it out of the room to the lab.

His guests eyed him suspiciously. "Doesn't the word 'genius' *mean* anything these days?" Lex asked. Then he walked to the curtains and flung them open, revealing the breathtaking view of Metropolis and a sparkling sunny day. Lenny returned with a cushioned case containing the remaining genetic material.

"Boys," Lex said, addressing the three criminals who adorned his conference table the way rubies adorn a crown. "Old Lex has a secret recipe in this dish — a sort of genetic stew. You help me place it on one of your missiles, and I promise you that if Superman throws it into the sun, he'll get the biggest surprise of his life. I will personally introduce him to his first nightmare — a Nuclear Man!"

"Why should we make a deal with a notorious scoundrel like you?" DuBois asked, speaking for all of them.

"Don't, then," Lex suggested. "Then the world will have eternal peace, and you boys will have to find day jobs. But, as long as the world hangs on the brink of war, the good life is available to every criminal — regardless of race, religion, or national origin!"

That was something they could understand.

"And what do you get out of it?" Howler asked.

"If my plan works, gentlemen, I'll just take a tiny commission. Something appropriate — perhaps a number with a *lot* of zeroes after it."

The deal was struck.

And when Superman threw his next load of nuclear missiles into the solar inferno, delivery was made. Harry Howler had managed to secrete the genetic material onto one of the missiles Superman selected for destruction. Little did Superman know the destruction might be his own.

As Superman returned to Earth's atmosphere, the explosion on the sun took on a new intensity, flames licking millions of miles into the sky, burning with a violent fierceness. The eruption built to a tremendous crescendo, finally jettisoning a ball of fire that tumbled through the blackness toward Earth.

As it spun, its shape altered. No longer amorphous, it elongated, and soon took a humanoid shape — legs and arms emerging from the mass of body — stretching, reaching for Earth, driven by genetic memory to an unknown destiny.

Finally, the full-grown creature broke out of its cocoon and flew free. It was a magnificent specimen. Its rippling sinews glowed with the heat of atomic fusion. Its muscles pulsed eagerly, flesh gleaming in the bright sunlight of Earth's atmosphere.

For a moment, the creature paused in the air and examined himself, admiring his own savage beauty.

Then he turned and flew toward Metropolis. For he had promises to keep.

Chapter 18

A little bit later the same day, Clark was fulfilling a promise to Lacy for his series on young Metropolis. They were at the city's trendiest health club, populated by the young, beautiful, rich people of Metropolis. While that group certainly included Lacy Warfield, it most certainly did not incorporate Clark Kent — and he was in no position to explain to Lacy that, as Superman, he hardly needed to work out. Oh, perhaps to move a mountain now and again, but he wouldn't benefit from aerobic dancing.

Which was where he was right then.

Lacy was garbed in a sleek exercise suit with matching tights. She moved easily to the disco beat, confidently following the instructions of the chic young teacher. Clark stood beside Lacy, wearing a baggy sweatsuit and basketball sneakers. The disco beat eluded him. When the teacher told the class to turn right, Clark turned left. When she told them to follow her movements, he couldn't see them because his glasses had fogged up in the overheated room. What it came down to was that Clark was a klutz.

"Maybe I should sit this one out," he said to Lacy.

"Don't give up!" She shouted encouragement. "This is a perfect subject for your new series on young Metropolis. They're all here! Now, let's get those knees *up!*"

Obediently, Clark followed her instructions. But the harder he tried, the more he looked like an uncoordinated orangutan.

Later, in the Nautilus room, things didn't go any better. Lacy tried to show him how to use the overhead pull bar.

First, Lacy adjusted the weights. Then she sat on the bench and reached for the handlebars above her. She pulled down, easily bringing them to her chest, and then raised them again, setting the weights back in their stack. She did it ten times while Clark watched.

When she was done, she stood up, and adjusted the weights, downward, for Clark. "We'll start you off with sixty pounds," she told him.

He sighed and sat in her place. As she had done, he grasped the handlebars and pulled. Nothing happened. He gritted his teeth and pulled again, raising himself up out of the seat. The weights budged. He locked his toes under the footrests for leverage. Straining and grunting, he managed to lift the weights eight inches — until he lost his grip on the handlebar. When that happened, the tumbling weights acted as a catapult, yanking Clark out of the seat and tossing him onto the floor of the gym.

One of the club's more frequent visitors, Paul, came over to watch. He pretended to offer help. Clark looked suspiciously at Paul's offered hand. Paul's perfectly contoured body bespoke hours of work on Nautilus machines. His bronzed skin was surely the pride of a local — and probably trendy — tanning salon. It had certainly taken precision to achieve the fashionable casualness of the sun-bleached and blow-dried look of his hair. Clark hated him on sight.

"I guess your friend doesn't know his own strength." Paul snorted with hilarity at his own humor, and at Clark's failure.

Lacy introduced Paul to Clark.

Paul was under the impression that the fun was just beginning. He reached for a bar with four thirty-pound weights attached and lifted it quite easily with both hands. "Want to try this one, Clark?" he offered, smirking.

"I don't think so," Clark said politely.

Undeterred, Paul handed the weight to Clark, who immediately followed it to the floor. The thump brought laughter from the whole room at Clark's expense.

"No pain, no gain," Paul said smugly and then sauntered out of the room.

"He's a jerk," Lacy said. "I never noticed it before. Seems like a lot of people I know are jerks these days. Maybe you think the same thing about me. That's why you keep avoiding me."

"I'm not avoiding you, Lacy. I've been very busy and I like you. I really do." Lacy would never know how busy he had been. It was too bad, Clark thought. It would be the scoop of her career!

"Then prove you like me!" she challenged him. "Lois is interviewing Superman about his peace mission. It's going to be at my hotel suite this evening. You come, too."

How could he refuse? But how could he accept? He was trapped!

"In fact," Lacy continued. "Come early! The view is spectacular!" With that, Lacy exited to the women's locker room, leaving Clark horrified and confused.

"Lacy!" he protested, almost unaware that Paul had reappeared, prepared to make a fool of him again.

"Say, Clark," Paul leered. "Could you hand me those weights? They're very light."

Clark's mind was riveted to the problem about Lacy's invitation. Distracted, he picked up a two-hundred-fifty-pound weight and tossed it easily to Paul. When the weight struck him, Paul flipped backward, crashing into the floor, to be pinned by the barbell. The look on his face was total astonishment.

"No pain, no gain," Clark told him.

Chapter 19

Lex Luthor awaited the results of his experiment. This time, it wasn't going to crash through his laboratory wall. It was going to come from out of the blue.

He paced back and forth on the terrace of his apartment, barely aware of the panoramic view it afforded of Metropolis. Lenny paced in his wake.

"Hey, Uncle Lex, how's the nuclear guy going to find his way here?"

Lex was pleased to have the chance to boast about how clever he had been. "When I sent the remains of my last experiment, I included the creature's genetic memory. He'll remember everything that he experienced. Not to worry. He'll find his way back to me."

There was a swoosh.

"Did you hear that?" Lex asked.

Lenny looked dumbly at the sky. "You're spooking me out, Uncle Lex," he whined, but then, he listened, too. It was unmistakable. Something was approaching.

In a flash, he arrived — the new and improved Nuclear Man. Lenny was awestruck, recalling the genetic pool that had engendered this bronze Adonis. "Hey! He looks normal!"

Lex circled his new creation, admiring every sinew, every perfect muscle. "I'm *incredible!*" he said, once more overcome by his own brilliance. "Welcome back home, Nuclear Man," he greeted the reincarnated evolutionary miracle, escorting him into his apartment from the terrace. "Your father is happy to see you."

Nuclear Man's face shone with confidence — almost a frightening degree of confidence.

"Let's test the old reflexes first," Lex said, casually prodding Nuclear Man with a steel ruler. Nuclear Man's eyes glowed red with anger. The ruler melted like milk chocolate on contact with his skin. He hissed and flung the dripping remains of the ruler off the terrace.

Lex's mind raced, and then he understood where this incredible power had come from. "I hadn't counted on this, but the power of the sun has given him internally generated heat. He's a walking nuclear oven! I am a — " Lex was dumbstruck by his genius.

"You are — " spoke Nuclear Man, as if to finish Lex's sentence.

"What?" Lex asked, curious about Nuclear Man's opinion of his creator. "A genius? An inspiration?" Lex suggested.

"You are nothing," Nuclear Man told him, bursting the balloon. "I am father now!" he boomed.

Lex took charge. "Hey! Just remember *I* made *you*!"

Lenny took up the pace. "You're just an experiment, *freako!*"

Nuclear Man regarded Lenny coolly — as coolly as possible considering the four thousand degrees his body could generate on request. He raised his hand and pointed to Lenny. Lenny stopped frozen in his tracks, and before he knew what was happening, began to rise off the ground. Nuclear Man made a casual circular gesture with his hand. Lenny began spinning in midair, slowly at first, and then vigorously, flying around the room in huge circles. Nuclear Man shrugged off Lenny's protests and turned his attention to Lex.

"I am an experiment? I am a freako?" he asked.

"I made you," Lex told him. "And I can destroy you."

"Destroy," Nuclear Man said in echo — a word he knew, but couldn't place. "Destroy."

Lenny circled his uncle and Nuclear Man. Both were oblivious of his pain and confusion. He shouted out, "I was just goofing around!" and then he was too far away to hope to capture Nuclear Man's attention. He waited until he approached Nuclear Man on the next pass. "Nobody's a freako around here!" he tried. No response. On the third pass, he tried again. ". . . but me!" he said.

But Nuclear Man didn't hear him. Suddenly, his genetic memory kicked into gear. "Destroy — destroy — Destroy Superman! Now!"

He released Lenny, who came crashing to the floor.

Lex noticed Lenny writhing painfully on the floor. "What are you doing?" he asked, without sympathy.

"Didn't you see it?" Lenny asked. "He lifted me up and crashed me down!"

Lex was interested — not in his nephew's difficulty, but in his creation's skill. "Hmm, nuclear levitation. Now that's a trick that could come in handy," he said.

Both of them stepped into the vestibule of Lex's lair, the small hallway leading away from the brightly lit main room. Nuclear Man followed them — up to a point.

When he reached the darkened hallway, leaving behind the last shaft of sunlight from the main room, he stopped in midstep, frozen. Lex looked behind him and saw this. Concerned, he walked back to Nuclear Man and touched him.

"He's cold!" Lex said.

"Good, let's hope he stays that way!" Lenny said. It would be a long time before he could forgive Nuclear Man for treating him so badly — after he'd risked his life to collect the genetic goo from the transformer fire, too!

But Lex was lost in thought, until the explanation — the only possible explanation — dawned on him. "Of course!" he said. "That's his one vulnerability! The only way he can be stopped!"

"Who?" Lenny asked.

"Lenny, my loud-mouthed nephew, he gets his power from sunlight! In darkness, he's like you: Useless!"

Chapter 20

It was a warm summer evening in Metropolis. It would be hours yet until the sun set. Lois opened the balcony door to Lacy's hotel suite to provide a lovely view of the city for their dinner guests — and to give Superman a way to enter.

Lacy was wearing an elegant silk dress, tight in just the right places. She hoped Clark would like it.

"This is just like a double date!" she said excitedly to Lois Lane, who was examining herself critically in one of the suite's full-length mirrors. "How do I look?" Lacy asked.

"Illegal," Lois told her frankly. "Just like you looked in the six other dresses you tried on. Believe me, no matter what you wear, Clark will not notice."

Lacy didn't believe her.

There was a knock at the door. "Clark!" Lacy

said, and then contained her excitement. "Or maybe it's Superman."

"Superman likes to make a different kind of entrance," Lois reminded Lacy.

It was Clark. He had had to plan long and hard to figure out how he and Superman could both be at Lacy's suite at the same time. It was going to be touch and go — fast!

His first excuse to get out of the suite was that he needed change for the cab. While Lacy went for her purse, Clark chatted with Lois. She showed him the list of questions Mr. Warfield had provided for her to ask Superman. " 'Are you or are you not a part of a plot to weaken our national defense?' " Clark read from the sheet.

"It's her father's brain that's weakened, if you ask me. How can I ask Superman such a dumb question?" Lois moaned.

"Politely?" Clark suggested.

Then, Clark took the change Lacy gave him and told them he would go pay the cab. As soon as the door was closed, however, he headed for the fire escape and, before Lois could comb her hair one more time, there was a rush of air on the balcony.

"What's that?" Lacy asked.

"Our other dinner guest," Lois said.

"Hi, Lois," Superman greeted her. "It's been a long time."

Lois's heart jumped. No matter how many times she saw him, every time was like the first time. Every time was wonderful. On the surface, Lois was a tough reporter, ready to fight toe to toe with the best of them to get her story or to find the truth. The word "hard-boiled" had been used more than once to describe her, and Lois was proud of it. But when it came to Superman, she was all soft and fluffy. All the sharp edges gone. She was in love.

As soon as Lois recovered her composure, she introduced Lacy to Superman and then suggested they start the interview without Clark. Superman breathed a silent sigh of relief, until Lacy threw a cog in the works.

"I'd better fetch Clark," she said. "He's probably helping the cab driver change a flat tire or some other good deed."

That was Superman's cue for another switch, but first, he had to figure out how to leave politely — or invisibly. Lois was no help at all. She took his arm and invited him into the suite's living room.

"We'll be more comfortable in here," Lois said, sitting next to him on the white brocade sofa. Superman sat down, unsure what his next move would be until his super-sensitive smell told him something was cooking in the little kitchenette off the living room.

"Something smells wonderful," he said.

"Just a little duck and scallops in champagne sauce, in case we get hungry later," she said as casually as she could. There was a part of Lois, the soft and fluffy part, that believed that the fastest way to a man's heart was through his stomach. She was sure Superman's heart was no different from any mortal's.

"I hope it wasn't too much trouble," Superman said.

"Of course not," Lois assured him. "Now, the first question — " As Lois spoke, Superman listened, but he also worked on his own plot. He carefully focused his heat vision on the oven, raising the temperature from a moderate 375 degrees to 650 degrees. While he watched, the dinner began bubbling at a ferocious rate. " — and have you had any trouble confiscating the missiles?"

"Well, Lois, there is always the chance that a few warped individuals — "

"Oh, my!" Lois leaped to her feet, the odors of almost overdone duck wafting out to the living room. "Don't budge! I'll be right back."

Superman budged.

Just a few seconds later, Lacy ran into Clark in the lobby of the hotel. She linked her arm through his affectionately and led him to the elevator that would lead him back to trouble. But when the doors opened, help was at hand. A bellboy swung a large luggage-laden dolly into the lobby, past Lacy and past most of Clark. Just at the last second, Lacy saw that Clark's sleeve had gotten caught on the dolly. Clark was completely helpless to extract himself and the elevator doors closed, whisking Lacy upstairs alone.

Clark headed for the revolving door.

Shaking her head, Lois stepped back into the living room. "It's funny," she said. "I've never had duck turn out so perfectly, Superman. Superman?" Where was he?

"On the balcony," he said. Lois joined him there.

Until the doorbell rang. Lois left Superman on the terrace (she thought) to open the door and was surprised to find Lacy alone.

"Where's Clark?" Lois asked.

"He was getting on the elevator — and then this man with luggage, and oh, it's a long story," Lacy said, slightly annoyed.

"It always is with Clark," Lois consoled her.

Until the doorbell rang again. Clark stepped in. "Say, is dinner ready?" he asked. "I'm famished!"

"Let's sit down," Lacy invited him.

"Superman!" Lois called out to the balcony, but there was no answer. "I'll go get him," she said, but before she reached the door, there was a loud crash and the unmistakable sound of glass breaking. Lois rushed back to Lacy and Clark, who was, as usual, apologizing.

"Here, I'll help," Lois offered, sweeping crystal shards with a linen napkin. Clark left the room to clean his suit — he said.

"There, now we can eat," Lacy said, finishing the task.

"Except that now they're *both* gone. This is ridiculous!"

Superman stood on the balcony, unsure of his next move in this silly charade — until he heard a familiar voice — a too familiar voice. It was Lex Luthor.

The image of the man, and his voice, were being projected to Superman from a gigantic billboard on the street nearby. Superman stared in disgust at Luthor's smarmy smile. But he knew that wherever there was Lex Luthor, there was trouble. And trouble was what Superman was on Earth for.

"Don't worry, Blue Boy," Luthor said. "You're the only one who can hear me. It's my own frequency. Think of it as Lex-TV."

Superman listened with contempt. "I'm about to blow twenty stories off that building over there, give or take a few," Luthor said, pointing to Metropolis Tower.

Then, as suddenly as it had appeared, Luthor's image disappeared from the electronic billboard. Once again, it was flashing an advertisement for a soft drink.

No matter how despicable Lex Luthor was, Superman could not ignore him — nor could he risk the lives of innocent Metropolitans by doubting his deadly threat. Superman had to go.

Superman stepped back into the suite. "I'm terribly sorry, Lois," he said. "But an emergency has arisen. Please apologize to your guests. Good-night!"

He turned and left the suite as quickly as he

could. There was no time to waste.

The last thing he heard as he flew toward Luthor's trap was Lois's voice, pleading with him. "Wait! Take me! I'll cover it for the *Daily Planet!*"

Even when she was in love, she was still a reporter, after all.

Chapter 21

Superman circled Metropolis Tower, finding no evidence of the bomb Lex Luthor had promised. He wasn't surprised. He knew Lex would never announce a dastardly plan if Superman had a chance of preventing it. But he would announce such a plan if he thought he had a chance of netting Superman!

Cautiously, he circled again, this time, spotting Lex on the terrace of his skytop lair. Lex was wearing a silver brocade smoking jacket and carrying a bottle of champagne. He raised the bottle in salute to Superman. "Guess who?" he said coyly. "It's your old friend, Lex."

"Luthor, I suspect if you had actually planted a bomb, you'd be far away from here by now."

"Silly me," Luthor laughed. "How do I ever think I can fool the super guy? You're right: No bomb. I just knew you were too busy with the world peace bit to make a social call, so I tricked you."

"All right, Luthor. I'm here. Now tell me, why are you back in Metropolis?"

"Why? Because I want to be the first one to introduce you to the new kid on the block," he said airily.

At that moment, there was a blinding light from the sky, floating down from the sun, over the top of a skyscraper, heading straight for the terrace where Luthor and Superman stood.

The burst of light seemed to collect and assemble on the terrace between Lex and Superman, until it was clearly human in form, finally forging itself into all the glory of Nuclear Man. Superman switched on his X-ray vision so he could get a really good look — up close and personal — at this vision of radiant power.

"Look closely," Lex advised him. "Check out the cell structure. See anything familiar?"

"You've broken all the laws of man, Luthor. And now, you've broken the laws of nature! I assume you must have hidden a device in one of the missiles I hurled into the sun!"

Lex applauded Superman's deductions. "You know, Mr. Muscle, I'll really miss these chats we have together. Now that Einstein is dead, you're the only one who can keep up with me! Lenny! Oh, Lenny!" he called.

Almost instantly, Lenny appeared on the terrace, carrying two crystal champagne glasses. Lenny glanced at Superman, almost shyly. Then, suddenly boldened, he spoke to Superman. "Boy, are you gonna get it!" He smirked.

Lex opened the champagne suavely and filled two glasses. "Let's share a toast to you: A nice guy who's about to finish last." Superman shook his head, refusing the proffered glass. "I forgot," Luthor continued. "You don't drink on duty."

Angered by Luthor's mocking, Superman took a step toward him. But he was stopped immediately, for Nuclear Man issued the loudest, fiercest, most terrible roar ever heard on Earth. *"DESTROY SUPERMAN!"* he bellowed.

"Whoa, boy. Not yet!" Luthor contained him. "He's anxious to start," Luthor explained. "Isn't he adorable?" Superman knew that only a twisted mind like Lex Luthor's could find Nuclear Man adorable. And that twisted mind was so proud of its wicked achievement that he couldn't help boasting. "There I was," he explained to Superman. "For the first time in my life, I had no long-range truly devious criminal scheme. I suppose I thought that with you gone I could pull off anything."

"I'm not going anywhere, Luthor," Superman promised.

"I'll ignore that. So, anyway, I created a monster, but he didn't work nearly as well as you. He needed more energy, more power."

"Which explains why you sent his — my — genetic matter to the sun."

"Precisely! And then it came to me. My greatest plan ever. I made a deal with some minor league bad boys — arms dealers, renegade generals, you know the type. With you gone, we'll make a fortune rearming the world!"

"You'd risk worldwide nuclear war for your own personal financial gains!"

"Oh, no, no, my dear boy. Nobody wants war. I'd just like to keep the threat alive."

Superman regarded his adversary with hatred. "A mind is a terrible thing to waste, Lex Luthor. And you've wasted yours on this foul monstrosity. I'm taking you in!"

Superman reached for Lex, ready to deliver him back to his prison. But as he did that, there was a reaction from Nuclear Man — a nuclear reaction! Suddenly his eyes and skin started to glow and turn molten. His entire body became elastic, proportions distending horribly.

"Nifty, huh?" Lex asked. "Okay, *now* destroy Superman."

It was Nuclear Man's cue — the moment he'd been waiting for since his fiery birth. His eyes lit up, literally, and a wicked grin came across his malicious face.

"First, I have fun!"

Chapter 22

It didn't take Superman long to figure out what Nuclear Man's idea of "fun" was: It was to imperil the lives of innocent people!

Nuclear Man's first stop was in the Great Plains. Superman trailed him there, arriving in time to watch a tremendous and fearful bolt of lightning threaten a small town. But it wasn't lightning at all — it was Nuclear Man. He began to spin in the air and within seconds a terrible funnel cloud formed and began a deadly descent to the town. Superman knew that the forces Nuclear Man had generated could destroy the entire town!

Superman came to the rescue!

The first building in the tornado's lethal path was a farmhouse. It reminded Superman very much of his boyhood home in Smallville. He couldn't let that be destroyed! As he descended to the family's aid, he saw the farmer and his wife and two of their children battling the raging winds to reach their storm cellar.

"Where's Jenny?" the woman called out.

Her husband panicked. "She must still be in the house!" he cried, returning to save his young daughter from certain death. The winds forced him back from his home. He couldn't reach the door. He couldn't save his daughter. And then, he was knocked to the ground by the tornado, which lifted the entire farmhouse off its foundation. The airborne house rotated with the force of the storm.

Just at that instant, Superman arrived. "Jenny's inside!" the farmer cried, looking at the flying house. He didn't have to say it twice. Superman flew into the center of the tornado and began circling in the opposite direction of the twister, faster and faster until he was just a red and blue blur. Faced with an opposite and equal force, the tornado relented, slowing its rotation gradually, and permitting Superman to replace the farmhouse on its foundation. When it was settled, Superman slipped in the front door and brought the frightened two-year-old Jenny to the welcoming arms of her parents.

Jenny's mother cried with joy, but before she could thank him, Superman had gone. He had to find out what Nuclear Man's idea of "fun" was next.

It was at The Great Wall of China. Nuclear Man slipped away, down to one of man's greatest engineering achievements. While tourists fled in terror, Nuclear Man began pulling the wall apart, brick by brick, hurling hundreds of the age-old stones at Superman. The attack didn't affect Superman, but it endangered the tourists. One, running from Nuclear Man's destruction, slipped and fell off the edge of the Wall. Superman dashed to her rescue, catching her in midair. He returned her to her husband.

Nuclear Man, finished with his "fun" in China, fled back into space. Before Superman followed him, he repaired the damage Nuclear Man had done to the Wall. It had taken mankind years to build that section of it. It had taken Nuclear Man only a few minutes to destroy it. Superman repaired it in a matter of seconds and then shot into the sky after his enemy. It had all happened so fast, the tourists weren't sure it had happened at all.

Nuclear Man's next target was a peaceful seaside town near an inactive volcano. Nuclear Man's incredible radiant heat reactivated the volcano and, totally without warning to the people of the town, there was a deadly river of molten lava flowing toward them. Superman was drawn to the town by the frantic ringing of the town's churchbells.

When he saw the imminent danger, he sprang to action. With his super speed, he flew to a nearby mountain and then circled it so fast and so furiously that it was as if his very body were a buzz saw. Soon, the entire top of the mountain had been severed from its base. Superman lifted it up and carried it to the erupting inferno. He turned the mountain top upside down and dropped it, like a cork, onto the eruption, stopping it as suddenly as it had begun.

By then, Nuclear Man had fled again, ready to resume his deadly game of hide and seek. Superman paused only to blow a mighty blast of cold air on the lava that still crept toward the village. It froze immediately, becoming harmless for eternity.

Nuclear Man then led Superman to a military parade in Moscow. And, once again, Superman foiled his wicked purpose, saving the Soviet leaders from death at the hands of their own missiles.

Finally, Nuclear Man led Superman back to the city of Metropolis. While Nuclear Man had been completely incapable of foiling Superman, he had succeeded in tiring him. Causing trouble was easy. Repairing it was not. Nuclear Man was still fresh. Superman was showing signs of fatigue.

It was the moment Nuclear Man had been waiting for.

Nuclear Man lingered near the base of the Statue of Liberty. When he was sure Superman was nearby — near enough to become embroiled in his final deadly trap — he picked the entire Statue up off its base. Then, to Superman's horror, he lifted the gigantic Statue into the air over the busiest section of Metropolis and released it!

Once again, Superman sprang to the rescue

of Metropolis. Just before the Statue crashed onto the city's most populous crosswalk, where it would have crushed thousands of people within seconds, Superman caught it and hauled it back toward its base.

But, finally, Nuclear Man had the best of Superman. For he had hidden himself inside the Statue of Liberty and while Superman used every ounce of his remaining strength to replace the Statue, Nuclear Man flew off the Statue's observation deck and attacked Superman with his incredible burning claws.

Superman stumbled in midair, nearly dropping the Statue. For the first time in his life, he could feel mortal pain. Nuclear Man had pierced Superman's flesh!

Staggering and exhausted, he slid the Statue back onto its base. While he gasped for strength that would not come, Nuclear Man made his final attack.

He pivoted in a circle of terror, belting the spent superhero with such force that he was sent flying helplessly off into the sky, out of Earth's atmosphere. All that was left of him was his blue and red costume, which came fluttering down out of the sky, landing on the darkened torch of the Statue of Liberty.

"Home run!" cried Nuclear Man triumphantly.

Chapter 23

IS SUPERMAN DEAD?

read the *Daily Planet* headline the next day, over a picture of Superman's costume hanging limply from the Statue of Liberty. It was a question on the lips of many of Earth's citizens. How else could they explain his sudden and mysterious disappearance at the hand of Nuclear Man?

Lois Lane held the paper in front of her with one hand, barely able to believe the facts — and disgusted that the newspaper that employed her could even begin to suggest the vague possibility that Superman had been beaten for good.

With her other hand, she held the telephone. When Clark Kent's recorded message finished and the beep came, Lois spoke: "Clark, it's Lois. This is the fourth message I've left. Where *are* you?"

Nothing was going Lois's way, and she'd had enough of it.

She stormed into the City Room where David Warfield and Lacy preened over their success at the *Daily Planet*. They counted the thousands of extra dollars they would receive in revenue just because Superman was in trouble.

Lois had no intention of being part of any organization that benefited from Superman's suffering.

"This time, you've both gone too far," she fumed, slapping the newspaper down on the table. "From now on, you can print your rag without Lois Lane!" She paused to let that sink in. Her eyes lit on Superman's costume, neatly folded, like the flag from the casket of a war hero. "And, you certainly have no right to this!" Lois said, grabbing the costume. Before either of the Warfields could react, Lois stormed out of the office, barely noticing the men in pinstriped suits asking for Perry White. They didn't get any help from her. She shoved past them onto the elevator — eager to escape the foul smell that emanated from the owner's office. It was the smell of greed.

Things were going better, however, for Lex Luthor. Within hours after the rumors of Superman's death were whispered, and then shouted, around the world, Lex had secured appointments with the world's foremost arms buyers. His first stop was Washington, D.C.

In the same room where so recently they had monitored the depletion of the world's stockpile of nuclear warheads, the senator and the general and their associates met with Lex Luthor and Harry Howler.

"Mr. Howler," the senator spoke. "I will give your associate, Lex Luthor, one chance to explain why we should listen to him — a known international outlaw — instead of throwing him in jail forever! And investigating *you*."

Howler blanched. Lex stepped forward. "A reason why?" he said smoothly. "Superman tricked you!" There were astonished murmurs around the table. Lex continued. "Senator, I don't have to tell a smart man like you that 'world peace' is a Communist plot! How do you know that Superman actually destroyed everyone else's missiles?" Lex had hit a tender spot. "I don't believe you want to gamble with safety — the very existence of our country! We all know you guys have *some* missiles left. But do you have *enough*?"

He looked around the room, delighted with the genuine concern — perhaps fear was a better word — he saw on the faces of the sages of war. He continued. "Gentlemen, Lex Luthor is here to replenish your nuclear stockpiles. At a very affordable price. It's my way of saying 'forgive me!' "

The men heard him. He had them. The General Chief of Staff spoke: "Senator, if what he says is true, I must recommend we immediately go on full military alert. We have to watch the skies for any sign of a sneak attack. We can't afford not to heed Mr. Luthor's warning!"

It was music to Lex's ears.

And the following day, the same tune was played again, this time in another language.

Lex stood next to General Romoff in the Kremlin's Top Security Conference room. "I am proud to call this man comrade!" Romoff declared, putting his arm on Lex's shoulder.

Lex began: "Comrades, we all know 'world peace' is a capitalist plot!" What could they do but agree? Lex and Romoff walked out later with a very large order for warheads.

And the following day in Paris, Lex made another presentation — this time with Du-Bois, to a conglomeration of international weapons dealers. The cry was heard: *"Vive le Luthor!"*

They were playing Lex's song all over the world.

In Metropolis, at Clark Kent's apartment, things were not going so well. Clark lay on his sofa, unable to move. He listened numbly as Lois's voice came on his answering machine once again: "Clark, I'm getting a little ticked off. Where *are* you?"

Clark didn't answer. He couldn't. He looked once again at the pierced flesh on his hand. He shuddered and collapsed on the floor.

* * *

When Lex returned to Metropolis, he called his three favorite arms dealers to his apartment. In sharp contrast to the nervous state they were all in the first time they met with him, they were glowing and expansive.

"Lex, my friend," Howler began, speaking for all of them. "We all appreciate how you've supported us lately and, uh, in recognition of your hard work, we've decided to increase your commission to twelve percent!"

"Gee, guys, that's swell of you," Lex mocked him. "But, actually, I've got another idea . . . ." He snapped his fingers. Nuclear Man stepped into the room.

Lex stood up. "Gentlemen," he said. "I've decided to assume full control of all your operations. As my first official act, you're fired. And, according to my calculations, your share of the profits comes to. . . ." He paused, pulling a scratch pad from his pocket and producing a pencil. "Now, let's see," he mumbled, scribbling on the pad. "Put down the five and carry the one. Then that's one, three is four, and six is ten, carry the one. Plus eight and eight makes — so we move the decimal two places and, in round numbers, your share of the profits comes to Zero. Zip. *Nada!*" He gleamed at his shocked guests.

"You're mad!" Romoff declared.

Lex snapped his fingers again. Nuclear Man held out his arm. In an incredibly simple display of power, Lex used Nuclear Man's arm as a cigar lighter. The cigar burst into flame. Romoff cowered at the demonstration and fled from the room. The other two followed close on his heels.

"Nice bit," Lex said to Nuclear Man. "They were really afraid after the cigar trick."

"And what are *you* afraid of, Lex Luthor?" Nuclear Man asked.

"Me? Now? With Superman dead and you on my team? What *could* I have to fear?" he asked.

"Destiny," Nuclear Man said ominously.

Chapter 24

Clark stood at the kitchen sink in his apartment. First he splashed a few drops of water on his face, hoping to stimulate himself. Then he filled a glass with water and drank. He drank deeply, seeking desperately to quench a thirst that perhaps nothing on Earth could help.

Suddenly, he was aware of a knock at his door, and then a frantic scratching. Someone was trying to break in! Clark stumbled toward the door, wondering if he even had a chance of protecting himself from an intruder. But before he reached the door to put on the chain lock, the door sprang open, and in stepped Lois Lane, carrying a small package wrapped in brown paper.

"Lois!" Clark recoiled in surprise. "What are you doing here?"

A fast look at Clark's pale face, and Lois knew he was in trouble. "You're ill! I knew it!"

Ever the mother, Lois led Clark back to his

couch. She laid the package on his coffee table and felt Clark's forehead for a fever.

"It's just the flu, really," he protested. "How did you know?"

"You haven't been at work. You didn't call the office. You didn't even call *me*." The latter, of course, was the greatest sin in Lois's eyes.

Clark sat helplessly at her onslaught, too weak to answer. Lois could see that he really couldn't tell her what was up.

"All right, whatever it is, I'm sure you've got your reasons. But somehow, something pulled me here. I've always known, when Superman is in trouble. . . ."

Lois's voice trailed off. For perhaps the hundredth time, Clark wondered if his other identity had been revealed, if Lois's clever investigative mind had unveiled his deepest secret. Now, he was almost too weak to care.

"Has something happened to Superman?" he asked.

Lois shook her head sadly. "Everyone's saying he's dead." She could barely say the last word. "I know in my heart that isn't true. He just needs help."

For the first time since his battle with Nuclear Man, Clark smiled faintly. "You know him so well — But I'm sure he'll manage. Wherever he is."

Lois looked at Clark, knowing the time had come to share her true feelings with someone — and who better than her close friend and colleague, Clark Kent? "But if he couldn't manage — I mean if Superman really were in trouble, then I'd want to tell him some things. I'd want him to know that I love him and that I'll always love him. And, no matter what happens on this planet, I know he tried his best to help us."

Clark held Lois tenderly, consoling her in her sadness, drawing a strength she would never know from her words. "I know he would thank you, Lois," he told her. "But now, if you'll excuse me, I'm very tired. I must rest. By myself. Please, Lois?"

Reluctantly, she stood up to leave. She gave Clark an affectionate hug. "Feel better soon," she said, fighting back tears. "And, if you should see him, or hear from him, he might need that," she said, pointing to the package on the table. The door closed behind her.

Clark opened the package slowly, deliberately. The familiar blue and red of Superman's costume spilled out of the paper, dropping onto the floor.

Chapter 25

Clark stood in front of the mirror in his bathroom. The face he saw reflected there was unfamiliar. It was his, but it wasn't. He regarded it closely. There was something different. It wasn't just the three days of beard or the pale tinge to his skin. He was seeing something he had never seen before. He was seeing vulnerability.

He looked at his hand, holding it up to the bright fluorescent light. There was the wound where Nuclear Man had scratched him. It seemed almost ironic to him that humans, who were so weak compared to him, could suffer many cuts and heal easily. Yet he, their Superman, seemed unable to heal from a tiny scratch. It was as if his very life were draining from the small wound.

Clark looked in the mirror again. Something had changed. Suddenly, his skin seemed too big for him, then it became wrinkled and his complexion sallow. His hair turned gray and thinned while he watched. He was aging!

Clark gasped to see it happen. He could hardly believe it was true, but the mirror was not lying. He could feel the burden of the failure of his own body, and it terrified him. Helpless to stop the deterioration, he cried.

First, there were only a few tears, and then he began to wail in pain and sorrow. He understood that his inevitable death would mean the failure of everything Superman stood for. Without him to prevent it, Lex Luthor would see to it that the world bent to his wishes and followed *his* dreams. Without Superman to prevent it, Lex Luthor would rule the world with terror and fear.

Clark knew that Pa Kent had been right when he'd told him that he had been sent to Earth for a reason, and the reason was to fight for freedom and justice for all the people of the world. That was a basic tenet of Kryptonian philosophy that Clark had learned from the crystals of knowledge that had come with him from Krypton.

Krypton. Yes, that was the only possibility.

Clark could hear Jor-El's words, so recently spoken from across the years and across the universe. ". . . All that remains of Krypton's energy is yours. After it is gone, you will belong solely to your new home."

Clark went to his closet. In the back, on the top shelf, was the Kryptonian energy module that he had taken from the vessel the last time he was in Smallville. He removed it from the box and held it in his hand.

Clark was almost too weak to walk. With his final remaining energy, he stumbled to the roof of his apartment building, carrying the module. The starry night above held a promise Clark feared he could not fulfill even with the help of the module.

Clark clicked on the switch of the module and waited. An eerie green light emanated from the module and a soft hum began — familiar, but unfamiliar. Clark watched and listened.

Once more, he heard his father's voice. ". . . If our dying planet can save your life, my son, we have not died in vain."

Clark felt his body drawing life-giving energy from the module, and then he lost consciousness.

The module's hum faded to silence, and the green light dimmed, flickering to blackness.

Chapter 26

The next morning, the dawn sun reached Lex's skytop apartment, giving its daily dose of strength and vigor to Nuclear Man. With the first rays of day, his radioactive blood began to circulate. He was ready for whatever evil the day might bring.

Awake and ready for action, he looked at the morning's issue of the *Daily Planet*, which lay on the breakfast table next to Lex's huge stack of cash. There, on the front page of the *Daily Planet*, was a picture of Lacy Warfield. The headline read:

NEW PUBLISHER FOR YOUR FAVORITE PAPER

Once again, Nuclear Man's genetic memory served him. He recognized Lacy right away, though he had never met her — in his present form. But his previous incarnation had fallen in love with her at first sight at the opening of

The Metro Club while she danced with Clark Kent. Even now, he could recall her dazzling beauty. Even now, it made his nuclear heart beat faster. Even now, he was in love.

He reached for the newspaper, but so hot was his love for Lacy that the paper burst into flames at his touch.

"Good morning, good morning!" Lex announced, sounding like a camp counselor trying to whip an unruly cabin into shape. "We've got a heavy schedule," he announced to Nuclear Man and to Lenny, who had followed him into the room. "I want to show you off to a few world leaders. We're expanding into the insurance market. I'll insure them against you!" Lex chuckled wickedly. He pulled up a chair to the breakfast table, admiring the mountain of cash he had stacked there. He breathed deeply. "I love the smell of money in the morning."

Nuclear Man trained his nuclear vision on the stack of cash, immediately turning it to an inferno. Before Lex's eyes, hundreds of thousands of dollars became ash.

Horrified, Lex cried: "Stop! I command you! You, you — " He searched for a word. *"Mutant!"*

"I am master now," Nuclear Man told him. His voice was so threatening that Lex couldn't doubt it. "Wait for my return," Nuclear Man announced. "I will bring back the girl."

Lex was too upset about the cinders, which were all that remained of his fortune, to notice that Nuclear Man had left. He did what any red-blooded greedy lout would do. He cried.

"Gee, Uncle Lex," Lenny said. "I thought you could control that nuclear guy! You really blew it, huh?"

"Shut up, Leonard," he said.

At that moment, Lacy was having a heated argument with her father in the publisher's office at the *Daily Planet*.

"Tone down our headlines?" Mr. Warfield bellowed.

"I'd just like to have a little less sensationalism," she told him firmly.

"Less sensational papers go broke, young lady. I taught you a long time ago that the business of newspapers is business."

"No, Daddy. Our business is responsible journalism!" Somehow, Lacy was finding it easier and easier to challenge her father. Somehow, she was acquiring ideals she'd never had before, feelings of responsibility to something other than Money and Success. These, she knew, were feelings her father had never felt — nor could he understand them.

Just then, there was a tremendous noise — a rumble and a roar — and the room shook. To Lacy and Warfield's horror, the concrete and bricks that separated them from the outside suddenly seemed to melt. When the melting stopped, there was a huge hole in the wall, through which stepped Nuclear Man!

"What is it?" Warfield demanded. But Nuclear Man's answer was a swat that sent War-field against the far wall, where he landed unconscious. Nuclear Man walked straight to Lacy, radiant joy glowing from every pore. He led her to the hole in the wall and, grasping her tightly, took her to the air.

"Daddy!" Her scream echoed off the sky-scrapers of the city, but he couldn't help her.

Nobody could help her.

Chapter 27

With the destruction of Superman and the capture of Lacy, Nuclear Man had accomplished everything lingering in his genetic memory. He was now free to do what he wanted. And what he wanted was to have fun. Nuclear Man's idea of fun was nuclear fun.

"I will return for you," he promised, leaving her with Lex and Lenny.

"Never!" she said, slapping his face.

"You are pretty when you're angry," he told her, leering. And then he left.

Standing on Lex's terrace, Nuclear Man drew strength from the sun and changed his body until his flesh became steel — the steel of a nuclear missile!

"Are you crazy?" Lex asked him, suddenly realizing what he was doing. "If you go flying shaped like that, you'll start a war. There will be nobody left on Earth except you, a beast — " Then Lex glanced at Lacy and understood " — and a beauty."

Of course, that was what Nuclear Man wanted: the nuclear destruction of all life on the planet, leaving only himself and Lacy.

Nuclear Man lifted off, bound on his deadly mission.

At the Pentagon, they spotted Nuclear Man almost immediately. He was an unidentified blip trailing across a radar screen.

"Do we have identification?" the Chief asked.

"It's not ours," the technician told him. "And" — he pressed his headphones closer to his ears — "they say it's not theirs, either."

The somber-faced men in the room exchanged glances.

"Can we risk launching our own missiles?" one asked.

"Can we risk *not* launching?" another countered.

And that was the question: If that unidentified missile was from the enemy, they *had* to reply in kind. If it wasn't an enemy missile, what was it?

On the other side of the globe, three Russian generals huddled over another radar screen.

"What if it's not theirs?" one asked.

"But what if it is!"

"We haven't given ourselves any other choice," the third told them soberly. "Prepare to counterattack."

They prepared.

* * *

Lex Luthor was always prepared for contingencies. He cleared the important papers from his desk while Lenny dragged two suitcases toward the elevator.

"Don't worry, honey," Lex told Lacy. "I'm sure he'll make a swell husband. If you need us, we'll be five hundred feet underground waiting for the nuclear winter to turn into nuclear spring."

The elevator bell rang, announcing its arrival. Lenny lugged the suitcases to it. But when the door opened, there was a surprise: "Uncle Lex! It's Superman!" Lenny choked.

"Superman, but you're — you're dead!" Lex uttered.

"Still having delusions, Lex Luthor?" Superman asked, striding into Lex's apartment.

Before Lex could answer, Lacy ran over to Superman. "The monster is going to start a war!" she cried.

At that moment, Lex realized that the only hope he — and everybody else — had for survival was, in fact, Superman. Superman was the only one on Earth who had a chance of beating Nuclear Man.

"Uh, right," Lex told Superman. "You've got to stop him. He's mad! I did what I could, but he's kind of lovesick for the girl. Boy, am I glad to see you. I've learned my lesson, too. I'm siding with the good guys from now on."

Superman knew exactly how much of that

he believed. "I'll deal with you later, Luthor," he promised. Then, he turned to Lacy. His face showed rock-steady dedication and earnest concern. "I have no right to ask you this. It could be dangerous," he began.

"Ask me," she interrupted him. "It's about time I did something for someone else."

Then Superman told her what he needed her to do — what the world needed her to do.

In the Pentagon, it was a Red Alert and all systems were go.

"Ready to launch," the Chief of Staff said, his finger hovering near the button. "Ten . . . Nine . . . Eight. . . ."

In Moscow, it was the same: "Seven . . . Six . . . Five. . . ."

Superman had five seconds to save the world!

Chapter 28

Superman and Nuclear Man spotted each other at the same instant. Nuclear Man still embodied the deadly bomb that would touch off the war that would end the world. But Superman carried the only thing on Earth that could waylay Nuclear Man from his conflagration of the planet.

"Ready?" Superman asked Lacy.

"Ready," she assured him. "Let's see what I'm made of."

Thousands of feet above the ocean, Superman released Lacy and sent her hurtling toward a certain death. Only one thing could save her.

The instant Superman dropped Lacy, Nuclear Man stopped, suddenly reforming himself from the nuclear missile to humanoid.

This change was reflected simultaneously on radar screens around the world. "Stop the countdown! It's gone!" cried the technician in the Pentagon.

"All systems cease action!" cried the Soviet General, as if in echo.

Around the world, mankind sighed with relief.

Meanwhile, over the ocean, Nuclear Man and Superman raced to save Lacy. Superman knew that every motion he made, every action he took, could mean the difference between the survival or destruction of the world. Nuclear Man would not win this time!

As Nuclear Man had used Superman's compassion for the citizens of Earth to beat him in their last battle, Superman would turn the tide and use Nuclear Man's devotion to Lacy to save the planet.

In a sudden burst of speed, Superman dove toward the lapping waves of the ocean and caught Lacy at the last second before she would have been consumed by the freezing cold water. Then, just as quickly, he turned and left with Lacy, headed for Metropolis, Nuclear Man following in their wake, leaving a furiously boiling trail in the sea behind him.

When Nuclear Man reached Metropolis, he found only Superman, standing alone by the entrance to Metropolis Tower. Nuclear Man was desperate to find Lacy, and he burned with a desire for her. He burned so furiously, in fact, that a taxicab came to a screeching halt in front of him, astonished to see a flaming being standing in the middle of the street.

The cabdriver leaned out of his cab window, ready to give Nuclear Man a piece of his mind. Nobody, but nobody had a right to block traffic that way. He, in turn, failed to notice a little old lady who climbed calmly in the backseat of the taxi.

"Where is the woman?" Nuclear Man confronted Superman, oblivious of the cabdriver.

"Give it up. You'll never find her," Superman said calmly.

Nuclear Man roared in frustration, zapping white-hot X-ray beams at a nearby gas main, which exploded immediately, sending flaming debris around the street. Superman and Nuclear Man stood face to face in combat stance, unwilling to allow the slightest distraction that might give the opponent the upper hand. Around them, people screamed and ran from the fearful tongues of flame.

The little old lady spoke to the driver. "One-fifteen West Street," she said, and then sat back to enjoy the ride.

To everyone's horror, Nuclear Man levitated the taxicab.

Nuclear Man jiggled the cab ferociously. The driver was transfixed with terror, holding the steering wheel for dear life.

Waves of energy poured from Nuclear Man's fingers and a second cab rose into the air. The passengers and driver shrieked with terror. Then, one passenger slipped out through an open window, hanging precariously by the door handle. Superman jumped to his rescue, lowering him carefully to safety.

Blaring sirens announced the arrival of the fire department. Nuclear Man turned his attention to the red trucks, permitting the taxis to plummet back to Earth.

In the second taxi, relieved passengers scrambled from the backseat, hearts still thumping in horror. In the first taxi, the little old lady leaned forward and spoke to the driver.

"How much do I owe you, young man?" she asked.

Chapter 29

Superman looked up into the sky near Metropolis Tower just in time to be hit by a burst of energy that smashed him back through the doors of the Tower. Nuclear Man was putting on a ferocious demonstration of his powers in a violent confrontation with the Metropolis Fire Department.

When the police arrived, he took them on, too, lifting their blue-and-white car twenty stories in the air and smashing it into the side of the building with such force that it stuck, protruding over the sidewalk. The police inside were frozen in fear. Suddenly, the car jolted loose and began tumbling toward the street and sidewalk below. Superman leaped upward, catching the car before disaster struck the occupants.

Nuclear Man didn't try to stop him; he was having too much fun playing with the newly arrived SWAT team. Forty men hustled from

the back of a large van and deployed everything
they had. They began shooting. He melted their
bullets in midair and then did the same with
their weapons. The surprised team members
found themselves holding white-hot, dripping
steel. Then, done with the team, Nuclear Man
turned his attention to their vehicle. He flipped
it over and began making it spin with such fury
that its final occupant was flung from the vehicle right into Superman's arms. Nuclear Man
then mounted the overturned vehicle and began shooting bolts of deadly heat in all direc-
tions, destroying everything within his mur-
derous reach.

"Stop! Stop! You win!" Superman cried. "I'll
take you to her!"

These were the words Nuclear Man had
waited for. Apparently despondent in failure,
Superman took off for Lex Luthor's skytop
apartment. Nuclear Man followed close behind.
But when he arrived, there was no sign of Lacy.
There was only Superman, standing in front of
the closed doors of Lex's private elevator.

"Where is she?" Nuclear Man demanded.

"Far away from here and safe," Superman
told him coolly.

They faced each other ferociously. For an
instant, the barest measure of time, Superman
glanced over his shoulder, as if to be sure the
elevator doors were closed. It was the slip Nuclear Man had awaited. He lunged at Superman, felling him with a tremendous blow. Then

he started toward the elevator doors.

"No! Don't go in there! She's not in there!"

But Nuclear Man was sure Superman was lying. He wrenched the doors apart to find — nothing! Nothing but darkness.

While Nuclear Man lingered in the shadows of the darkened, empty elevator, Superman sprang to action, shoving him inside and closing the doors. Superman slammed his fist through the control panel, shorting the electrical circuits. Now he had Nuclear Man just where he wanted him: In the dark — permanently barred from his only source of power — the sun.

Quickly, Superman grabbed the elevator cable and pulled the entire mechanism high into the sky. Superman would take Nuclear Man to the darkness of the moon where he could no longer endanger the good citizens of Earth. Locked and powerless in the sunless world of the elevator car, he would atrophy. The world would be free of his brand of hatred and cruelty forever.

But there was something Superman didn't know. He didn't know that he had cracked the elevator car as he yanked it from the Metropolis Tower. He didn't know that the strain of leaving the earth's atmosphere made the little crack into a larger crack. He didn't know that each time the crack in the car swung around and faced the sun, the beams of light entered, delivering life-giving solar power to Nuclear Man.

Carefully and deliberately, Superman brought the elevator car around the moon's equator and set it down on the dusty terrain in the lunar night. Satisfied at a job well done, Superman circled the moon in preparation for his return to Earth. But as he was ready to take off, he paused at the Sea of Tranquility, site of the American astronauts' most recent visit to the moon. There, he saw that the American flag they'd left had been tilted, perhaps by the forces of their own ship, as they departed. Superman went over to the familiar red, white, and blue, and righted the flagpole, unaware that the lunar dawn was rising on the elevator car that contained the dormant Nuclear Man.

At first, there was only a small shaft of light shimmering through the small crack. Then, as the moon rotated further, the light became brighter and its beams struck Nuclear Man. It was the very medicine he needed.

Seconds later, he burst from the elevator car and attacked Superman, catching him unawares saluting the American flag.

Nuclear Man and Superman exchanged gigantic energy bolts. Each was able to deflect the other's volley easily. Then, Superman shot into the air and plunged down on Nuclear Man, attacking him with a massive two-fisted thump. Nuclear Man was ready, though, countering with his own forceful punches. After a short, but fierce battle, Superman downed Nuclear Man, for the last time, he thought, piercing

Nuclear Man's mortality as Nuclear Man had nearly done to his own.

Breathing deeply with relief, Superman paused to straighten the flag a final time. But Nuclear Man was not beaten. He leaped at Superman from behind, grabbing him in a deadly bear hug, then smashing him down into the moon rock, which buried him completely.

When Superman stopped moving, Nuclear Man kicked the American flag into the lunar dust and turned toward Earth.

"Laaaaaaccccyyyyy!" he cried, and took off for the vulnerable planet beyond.

Chapter 30

Superman scratched at the rough rocks and dust that entombed him. As he fought exhaustion, he had but one thought in his mind: Save Earth.

True, Nuclear Man had beaten him once again, but it was not their final battle. Superman knew that. Nuclear Man might have all the strength of Superman — and then some — but he didn't have Superman's wit and cunning. If only Superman could trap him in inescapable darkness. If only there were night all over the Earth. But Superman knew that wasn't possible. At least half the earth was always in the sun — except. . . .

Nuclear Man crashed through the ceiling of Lex's lair. There, he found Lacy Warfield, cowering in fear.

"Come!" he said to her. "You shall be my queen!"

Powerless to resist, Lacy submitted to the abduction.

On the moon's surface, Superman struggled to his feet and caught his breath. He had the answer now — the answer to his total, inescapable victory over Nuclear Man. He finally knew how to beat this enemy — how to win *and* to use him for good. Now, if only he had the strength to do it. A simple task: He had to move the moon.

Using every ounce of his super strength, gauging carefully, Superman moved the moon out of its orbit so that it sat exactly between the sun and Earth. Thus he created a total eclipse of the sun, darkening every corner of the earth at one time.

When he saw that his task was done — that Earth was in total darkness, he went in search of Nuclear Man.

He didn't have far to go to find him. Deprived of his source of natural energy, Nuclear Man dangled uselessly in space, immobile. Lacy was held in his ironlike clutch. Superman released Lacy and took her to safety in Metropolis. As long as the moon covered the sun, Nuclear Man was no danger to Earth.

Superman returned to the sky where Nuclear Man floated and brought him down to Earth, stopping over a nuclear power station. He hurtled Nuclear Man into the darkness of the cooling tower. Nuclear Man rocketed through an open hatch, which slammed shut and locked behind his inert body.

Suddenly, all of the power meters in the control section showed the plant at full charge! The city around blossomed with light.

In the eternal darkness of the power station's cooling tower, Nuclear Man's evil had been harnessed for the good of mankind.

Chapter 31

Lenny was at the wheel of the getaway car —
the car he and his uncle were using to get away
from Nuclear Man.

"You think he'll find us?" Lenny asked.

"Never," Lex assured him. "But we have to
hide out for a while — lay low for, say, a couple
of years. By then, I'll have a new plan."

"Lucky I brought my drums!" Lenny said,
displaying his new drumsticks.

Lex grabbed the drumsticks and tossed them
out the window.

Suddenly, there was a terrible shaking in the
car. It began to rise off the ground!

Lex and Lenny looked at each other. Lex
and Lenny each looked out their windows. Lex
and Lenny each saw Superman — holding the
car in the air.

A few minutes later, Superman delivered Lex
to the very same chain gang he'd escaped such
a short time before. As Superman hitched him

back into his own place on the chain, Lex shook his head in confusion.

"But, how could you beat him?" he asked.

"High school physics, Luthor," Superman said. "While I was recuperating, I had time to figure out that if your foul creature was born from the sun, it must have been his source of energy."

"But isn't the world about to be Osterized?"

"No. It's the way it always is: On the brink — with good fighting evil. Right now, though, with your return to prison, good's well ahead of the game!"

Then Superman left. His next step was to deliver Lenny to the nearest home for wayward boys.

"This boy's been under a bad influence, Father. Can you help him?"

"Every boy can be helped, Superman," he said, welcoming Lenny to his new home.

"That's what I think, too," Superman said, leaving Lenny in the good man's care.

In Metropolis, there was some major work going on with the sign at the *Daily Planet*. Several workmen in overalls were removing the giant steel plaque that read: WARFIELD PUBLICATIONS. Perry White watched the operation with glee. Lois and Jimmy stood nearby, a little nervous that their fearless leader had finally gone over the brink.

David Warfield's sleek limousine pulled up

to the curb and he leaped out, yelling as he came: "You'd better have a good explanation, White, or you'll be talking to your lawyers from jail!"

Perry winked joyfully at Lois and Jimmy and spoke to Warfield. "You know, I'm not a tycoon. I'm just an old reporter. But I've read enough in my own paper the last few years about hostile takeovers of companies. You must have been asleep at the wheel, Warfield, because I managed to convince the bankers of this city that the *Daily Planet* should be treated like a natural resource — protected from predators like you. They loaned me the money. I bought all the outstanding shares, and you, my predator friend, are now the *minority* shareholder."

Warfield's jaw dropped.

Just then, a panel truck drove past them, tossing a bundle of newspapers, hot off the press, onto the sidewalk. It was the *Daily Planet*. The old *Daily Planet* — and the headline read:

WE'RE BACK!

Lois and Jimmy hugged Perry with joy. Warfield slunk back to his limousine and left. For good.

Lois and Jimmy didn't have long to celebrate with Perry, though. They had to get to the United Nations, fast. The word was that

Superman was going to be back there for another announcement. Clark was supposed to meet them there, too, but they didn't see him when they arrived.

Clark was in a taxi with Lacy and a tremendous amount of her luggage. She'd just shared her news with him: She was done with Daddy's newspapers. She was done with big-city life.

"I'm going to find a place like Smallville in the country, maybe a farm. I want to see what life in the slow lane is like."

"I'm sorry to see you go," Clark said truthfully.

"You don't have to be polite, Clark. I have a pretty good idea of how you feel about me." She sighed. "Maybe if you'd met who I am now, instead of the spoiled brat you met a few weeks ago, it would have been different between us."

Clark began to protest. He'd learned a lot about Lacy Warfield recently — and she'd learned a lot about herself. She was a fine woman, and he admired her strength and courage.

"No, don't answer," Lacy said. "I want to consider the possibilities."

They both laughed, and then Clark spoke. "If you get to Smallville, I know a real estate agent. Levon Hornsby is his name." Clark reached into his pocket and produced the man's business card. "He may have the perfect place available. Tell him you know me."

Lacy took the card and smiled in understanding. The cab pulled away.

Clark smiled to himself, pleased. When Lacy bought the Kent farm, it would stay a farm, not become a shopping center. There had been a lot of changes in Lacy Warfield in the last few weeks. That was one of them.

Clark pushed his way through the crowd at the United Nations, finally spotting Jimmy and Lois.

"It must have been a super effort to get out of bed," Lois teased him, though she was relieved to see her friend feeling better.

"Well, my improvement was all because I had a good nurse," he told her.

"And you must have had some strong medicine," Jimmy piped in.

"Well, Jimmy," Clark told him. "Sometimes a little loving care is the best medicine."

It was getting too tender for Lois. There was business to be done. "I'm glad you're here," she said. "And don't forget, I'm covering Superman's press conference. You just tape reactions from people in the crowd."

"Oh, no!" Clark moaned, patting his coat pocket. "I left my new tape recorder in the taxi! I've got to get it back!" He disappeared in the crowd.

"Same old Mr. Kent," Jimmy grinned, shaking his head. "He'll never change."

"I hope not," Lois said.

Chapter 32

All over the world, people gathered around radios and televisions to listen to Superman.

He stood in front of the United Nations, this time speaking to the people of the world directly, not only to their delegates. It was a message for everyone.

"Once more, we have survived the threat of war. And once more we've found a fragile peace. I thought I could give you all the gift of freedom from war, but I was wrong. It is not mine to give."

He paused, waiting for understanding to come. The people needed to understand that peace was something they could only give themselves. Then he continued.

"Our planet is still young. What a brilliant future we can have! But there will only be peace when the people want it so badly that their governments will have no choice but to give it to them!"

There was a roar from the crowd. Superman knew that he was being heard.

"I wish you could all see Earth as I see it — Hey, wait a minute! Maybe you can! If you'll excuse me for one minute. . . ."

To the astonishment of the assembled crowd, Superman lifted himself aloft and flew away, leaving everyone confused.

But, he had his reasons.

A few seconds later, there was a *whoosh!* in the school yard above Jeremy's school. All the kids looked up and saw — Superman!

As soon as he spotted Jeremy, he landed. "I need your help, Jeremy," he said. Jeremy took his hand gladly, and together they flew above the clouds.

Jeremy gasped at the beauty of what he saw. Below was Earth, but it was as he'd never seen it before. At first, they were near enough for Jeremy to see the stunning beauty of rich farmlands, breathtaking mountains, glorious oceans, endless plains, and majestic ice caps. But as they drew farther and farther away, it was a single planet, blue and green, covered with wisps of clouds, spinning on its axis. It was more beautiful than any dream Jeremy had ever known.

"Awesome!" Jeremy whispered.

"Jeremy, I need you to tell the people of the world what you see," Superman said.

"I'll try," Jeremy said earnestly. And then he began his description. "Well, I see the ocean currents and the rain and the mountains and rivers, but — "

"Go on," Superman encouraged him.

"But you can't tell where one country begins and another one ends. You can't see any borders. It's just — one world."

Superman smiled proudly. That was just what he wanted to tell the people of Earth. "Good," he said. "If you can see it, and I can see it, maybe some day everyone will see it."

Together, they flew back to Earth. For they had promises to keep.